D1432598

THE COMING WATER FAMINE

Books by Jim Wright

The Coming Water Famine

You And Your Congressman

THE COMING
WATER FAMINE

Congressman Jim Wright

James Claud Wright III

COWARD-McCANN, INC., NEW YORK

For my wife, Mab

AUTHOR'S NOTE

Since time began, water and life have been synonymous. Water is the cheapest, yet the most priceless, of all commodities. Since the dawn of history it has given respite to the traveler, solace to the sick, succor to the land, reflection to the philosopher—and to the earth itself a never-ending renewal. No life can exist without it.

Water is twentieth-century man's most necessary servant, and we use it in copious quantities. In the United States today it takes 300 gallons of the indispensable fluid to produce a single loaf of bread. To grow a pound of beef and to get it to your dinner table requires at least 1,000 gallons of water. About 100,000 gallons go into the manufacture of each automobile. Almost everything we do reflects its use.

The harsh truth is that in the midst of unprecedented plenty America is running out of usable water—not slowly, but rapidly. No imaginable crisis could present a bleaker prospect. To tell that story is the burden of this book. The first five chapters explain what has been happening to us. In the last six I attempt to describe what belatedly we are trying to do—and what *more* we must do—if we are to avoid a water famine.

In attempting a treatment of a subject so vast, an author owes debts which go back to his earliest conscious aware-

5

ness. To try to recite them all would be prohibitive of time and space. A book on so vital a topic does not spring full-blown; it evolves.

Twenty-one years ago a remarkable conservation farmer, named Frank White, of Azle, Texas, stirred my interest in the subject. He foresaw, long before the hot hand of drought closed a fist upon America's East Coast, what could happen to our cities. I spent many hours in the fields with him, studying the behavior of water upon the land. He was, in the Old Testament sense, a prophet. Frank is dead now, and too many refused to listen to him; but this is his book.

My friend and mentor Conrad Russell taught me the meaning of water to the life of a town. He showed me in the lean years of Texas' seven-year dry spell how easily it can be wasted and how good management can husband it, purify it, and develop every available source. So this is Conrad's book.

James Dillet Freeman saw beyond the prosaic uses of water to its essential character. He said it well:

Water never resists, yet it wears away the most resistant things.

Water fits itself to conditions, takes the shape of any bowl it is poured into. Yet nothing shapes more things than water; the continents have the shape it gives them.

Water does work, but is never busy. It may turn a mill or light a city, but not by trying. Water lets itself be used.

Water has learned humility. It is colorless, yet what is a rainbow but water? It is tasteless, yet what is there better to drink? It always seeks the lowest place. But those in high places come to drink of it.

Sam Rayburn understood this and talked with me about it. So do my colleagues Bob Jones and John Blatnik and Ed Edmondson, who have discussed the subject of our water crisis with me in depth on many occasions. So does the League of Women Voters, an organization which has been crying in the wilderness for years, begging someone to listen. This is their book, too.

Even when you know what you want to say, it still takes many weeks of sifting and sorting, of ferreting out the unforgiving facts to be sure your book will tell the important truth with as much precision as possible. Bob Spence and Dick Stuckey helped me round up enough solid factual material to support ten books, and Gerald Cullinan helped me piece it all together so that it moves, like a partially tamed river, in a fairly straight line. A lot of this book is really theirs.

But you are the one for whom the book is written. If water famine comes, it is your children who will suffer. It then will be too late for reflections upon what we *should* have done. There'll be no comfort in hindsight, no satisfaction in placing blame. It's your country whose future is at stake. So I earnestly hope that this is your book, too—and that you'll make its burden your battle.

JIM WRIGHT

Washington, D. C.
March, 1966

Foreword

"Behold, I will smite with the rod that is in
my hand upon the waters which are in the river,
and they shall be turned to blood. And the fish
that are in the river shall die, and the river
shall become foul; and the Egyptians shall
loathe to drink from the river." (Exodus 7:17-18;
circa 1250 B.C.)

"Brush your teeth with the best toothpaste,
then rinse your mouth with industrial waste."
(Tom Lehrer, A.D. 1965)

Across more than 30 centuries, the author of Exodus and the
purveyor of ironic commentary on today have linked minds.

For water, if it was a matter of concern at the dawn of
civilization, is now a matter of the utmost urgency. In this
comprehensive volume, Congressman Wright has come to
grips with the key issues.

With half the world going to bed hungry, with croplands
wasting for want of the liquid living they require, one of the
direst dilemmas in the world today is how to conserve our
water supplies and make them serve man's vital purposes.

In the winter of 1965, for the first time in the memory of
man, there were no baby oysters in Long Island Sound. The
cause of this estuarial infanticide? Pollution!

But to talk of pollution as endangering only such species

as oysters is to talk speciously. For when man pollutes his water to the point where it is undrinkable—to the point where it constitutes an unfit environment for his own food supplies —then man himself becomes the "endangered species."

In this lively and highly readable volume, Congressman Wright has taken a worldwide, history-long look at the distribution, the use and ab-use of water on this earth. He has traced the death of such sparkling lakes as those that once graced Mexico City, and he has described the condition of rivers which now dis-grace our American urban scene.

To speak of "use and ab-use," of "grace and dis-grace," is to tell the story of water in the fewest possible words. To handle the story adequately, more words are needed and these words Congressman Wright has provided most eloquently.

Beyond words, however, lies the burning need for action. Such action as we have so far taken is described by the Congressman as too little and too late. Projected action, which is gathering momentum as recent Congresses have become increasingly aware of the disastrous implications of a no-action policy, is arrestingly described.

Unprecedented and continuing population and economic growth, increasing urbanization, and technological changes, all are major contributors toward a water problem which no longer can be ignored.

We are far behind the water clock in management and development and distribution of the liquid which is life itself. As President Johnson so aptly pointed out during the autumn of 1965, when the north and middle Atlantic coast water crisis passed into its fifth year, such bold, farsighted water management projects as have been building in the West for six decades are long overdue in other parts of the nation.

To call such projects "pork barrel," as they have so often and inappropriately been termed, is not only misleading—it is downright deceit. Far from being "pork barrel," they have turned out to be "rain barrel," and the plight of such cities as Philadelphia and New York has lent recent, dramatic evidence to this truth.

The distressing lag in Federal action to correct our water woes is systematically dissected by Congressman Wright and concrete suggestions for improvement are set forth. The main point here is that delay is simply no longer possible if we are to maintain even the standards which now prevail. Mounting demands on our finite supply of water are accelerating our date with a dry destiny.

Leadership has come from a President who knows firsthand the urgency of water conservation, from public officials in regions suddenly struck by near-disaster drouth conditions. But what is needed in addition is a citizenry alive to and aware of the need for stewardship, for planning, and perhaps above all, for spending. The solution will not be a cheap one. The problem has grown too great to be dealt with in piggy bank terms.

In this book, Congressman Wright has made a signal contribution toward public education in this area where adequate steps depend upon adequate information and widespread understanding. It is my earnest hope that this volume will be widely and thoughtfully read.

STEWART L. UDALL

Contents

1 Crisis Upon Us

"... where the sun beats
And the dead tree gives no shelter, the cricket no relief,
And the dry stone no sounds of water
... I will show you fear in a handful of dust."
— Eliot: *"The Waste Land"*

The United States of America, the richest and most powerful nation in the world, is running out of its most indispensable commodity. That commodity is clear, usable water. And unless we learn very quickly how to trap it, conserve it, share it, purify it and keep it unpolluted—and in some cases move it from one place to another—we soon are going to be in very desperate straits.

The problem manifests itself in many ways:

In a Connecticut public school, a new student tries the drinking fountain, steps back in disgust as a milky substance froths up in bubbles from the faucet. A classmate explains that it's a bad time of day to get a drink, because detergents are working their way back through the city's water system.

A growing western town adopts an ordinance against the installation of electric heating or cooling appliances, prohibits watering lawns except for two days a week. The community is only eight miles from a huge hydroelectric power reservoir, but it can't get permission to hook on and is running out of both water and power.

In the nation's capital, a father proudly takes his young daughter for a ride in a swan boat on the beautifully landscaped tidal basin, where cherry trees form a delicate pink wreath beneath the Grecian grandeur of the Jefferson Memorial. He looks away in embarrassment and suddenly changes the subject when his little girl asks, What are all those odd-looking things on top of the brownish water?

Dead fish float up to the banks of Town Creek in a small midwestern community, after a local shelling plant dumps its refuse, laden with tannic acid, into the stream.

In New York City, panic threatens as citizens are told, in the fourth year of subnormal rainfall, that the entire metropolis could be completely out of water in five months "if it doesn't rain." A fifty-dollar fine is imposed upon the offering of a glass of water in a restaurant, and residents are urged to take showers rather than baths and to take them as seldom as possible.

A UCLA professor warns his colleagues and the nation that the West is only fifteen years away from a disastrous water famine.

A West Texas town hauls water fifty miles in tank trucks for its citizens to drink, while an East Texas town feverishly fights a flood.

In big city suburbs, salesmen of distilled water report a fantastic boom in the sale of their product.

Three times in one week, a southern city seeking new industries is turned down because it lacks a "dependable" water supply.

An international crisis looms as an official Mexican delegation tells the U.S. Congress that our Colorado River irrigation system is dumping crop-destructive salt on the best farming lands in the Mexicali Valley.

All these are but a few facets of the most rapidly growing domestic headache in the United States: *We're running out of usable water.*

The problem, at first parochial, is very rapidly becoming national. Thousands of little and medium-sized local crises are merging into one huge national crisis. Within a very few years, every major section of the country will have serious water troubles of one type or another.

For the past twenty years, I have watched this situation develop. For the past fifteen, I have been actively engaged in efforts to combat the water shortage. In Northern Australia during World War II, I saw the major part of a continent, rich in ores and minerals and beckoning for development of its dormant treasures, perpetually held down by the dead hand of chronic drought. I returned from that experience thankful for the bounteous nature which had blessed our own land and its people.

But in the prolonged southwestern drought of the early 1950's, I learned from costly personal experience on a Texas Hill Country ranch how utterly dependent our own culture can be on the water supply, which in turn is so dependent on the vagaries of nature.

Fortunately for me and our family, I did not depend on the ranch for our primary livelihood. But many of our neighbors did. And when the pasture grasses died out for lack of water and the stock tanks dried up and crusted over, for

17

many it meant not merely inconvenience and short-term loss, but severe economic distress.

For four and a half years, I was mayor of a city which had to enforce water rationing, a city where a toast-brown lawn, fire hazard that it was, became a mark of good citizenship. For one of those years, as president of the League of Texas Municipalities, I worked with city officials in the other seven hundred cities which made up its membership as most of these struggled to catch up with the growing demand for water.

In 1953, I served as president of the local Chamber of Commerce at Weatherford, Texas. Like most communities, we were hungry for industry. But time and again, just as we thought we had a new payroll all sewed up, we felt the stranglehold upon our growth—the unsatisfiable need for more water.

Since coming to Congress in 1955, I have worked with others at the job of improving the nation's clean water supply. On the House Public Works Committee, we have launched the Water Pollution Control Act and expanded it. Congress has authorized $22 billion worth of water-resource developments throughout the country in the past decade. We have written laws encouraging local participation in federal reservoirs. Hopefully, we've embarked upon an experimental desalination program.

But all of these advances—valuable though they are—have merely delayed the day of reckoning. The problem grows faster than our efforts to defeat it.

The water famine is caused by people and by our advancing industrial society. We have been growing too rapidly to keep pace in the development of our resources, and have been too preoccupied with growth to think enough about conservation. We have abused the resources we have.

One of the most significant facts of our time is our population growth, both in the United States and throughout the world.

In the beginning, the world's population grew very slowly. At the start of the Christian era, there were only some 250 million people on the entire earth. It took fifteen hundred years for that figure to double, or reach 500 million. But then began a sudden and dramatic upswing which has continued over the past five hundred years. There were a billion people in 1835, two billion in 1935, three billion in 1965. If this pace is maintained, there will be six billion in the year 2000, or twice as many as we now have.

Here in America, when we sit down to dinner each evening, there are seven thousand more of us than on the evening before. Every year we add the equivalent of a new Philadelphia. The same amount of water must be made to serve more and more people.

Worse still, our society each year is using more water *per capita*. The whole nation required only 40 billion gallons daily in 1900. We used 360 billion gallons a day last year. On a per capita basis this comes out at 526 gallons per person in 1900, and 1,893 gallons per person in 1960. Unless we mend our ways, this figure will double by 1980 and triple before the beginning of the twenty-first century. We don't have anywhere near that much natural water.

As acute as the natural water shortage threatens to be, the

water pollution problem is worse. It is already on us and is rapidly debilitating the supply we have. Every section of the country is affected. Streams which once ran sparkling pure have become fouled by municipal sewage, by organic and industrial wastes which transmit disease, by toxic detergents and pesticides, by inorganic chemical and mineral substances which are spewed forth by mining, manufacturing, oil and chemical plants. And there is also the relatively new problem arising from radioactive wastes.

When demand exceeds supply, the *reuse* of water becomes a necessity. A special Congressional study in 1963 pointed out that the total dependable fresh-water supply available to the country by 1980 will be only about 515 billion gallons a day. But our total daily water requirement will have climbed to more than 700 billion gallons. Even with optimum foreseeable developments in purification and engineering, we cannot expect to have more than 650 billion gallons available, or 50 billion gallons a day less than our needs. And by the year 2000, our foreseeable water needs will exceed 1,000 billion gallons a day.

Obviously, therefore, the nation must rapidly complete engineering projects which will capture the maximum 650 billion gallons and find ways to treat and purify the water so that each gallon will be usable at least twice.

Today, in almost every stream, some water is used more than once. The waters of the Ohio River, for example, are used 3.7 times before reaching confluence with the Mississippi.

The pollution problem has been growing more rapidly than have our solutions. By the end of 1959, the municipal sewage released into our streams was equal in pollution effect to the untreated sewage from 75 million people. This is fully three times the amount of water spoliation the country was suffering as recently as 1900.

A landmark program was begun in 1956 with enactment of the Pollution Control Law. The act recognized federal responsibility in assuring the quality of the nation's water supply. It offered matching funds as an inducement for municipalities, burdened with bonded debt, to improve and modernize their sewage treatment facilities. Under this law, Congress has appropriated nearly $500 million. Almost $2.5 billion worth of new remedial projects have been stimulated by this law. A total of almost six thousand American communities by the beginning of 1966 had been assisted in making an intelligent assault upon their pollution problems.

Even so, the results are dwarfed by the continued and increasing need for more remedies. Every state health agency which processes applications for these federal matching grants reports there is a long waiting list of communities wanting and needing to get on with the job.

These pollution problems have been developing for many years, and they are gaining in intensity. The crisis of the summer of 1965 brought the problem suddenly and dramatically home to many who had never before thought about it seriously.

Long Hot Summer 1965

Many Americans were stunned in late May of 1965 when authorities in New York City, our greatest metropolis, pro-

21

hibited restaurants and similar establishments, under pain of severe fine, from serving a glass of water to a customer unless he specifically requested it.

Governor Richard J. Hughes of New Jersey went a step further. He decreed that the northern counties of his state could not serve water to diners, whether they asked for it or not.

In New York City, it was hoped that the ban against restaurants serving a glass of water might conserve 12 to 15 million gallons daily. This, in itself, would be trivial compared to the 1¼ billion gallons of water used by that city in an average summer day. But the ban had its psychological impact. New Yorkers, who get their tap water free of charge and had always been prodigal of it, learned suddenly that they were in deep trouble. The entire nation became more water-conscious.

The problem had been building steadily.

A drought of nearly four years' duration, the longest ever experienced by the northeastern tier of states, reached disastrous proportions in 1965. New York, New Jersey, Connecticut, Massachusetts, Maine, New Hampshire and Pennsylvania—an area containing one-fifth of our total population—faced the very real possibility of water starvation.

To make matters worse, the contagion of drought was spreading to the South. The states of Delaware, Maryland, Virginia, as well as the District of Columbia, were increasingly affected by the interminable dry period. No one could honestly predict relief in the immediate future.

This was a new problem for the East. In the West, of course, water shortages have been a way of life for generations.

In New York City, the ban on the restaurant water-glass was extended rapidly to other uses and users. No longer were children in the crowded tenement areas permitted to frolic in gushers of water from fire hydrants, their traditional relief from the torrid city summers. Flowing fountains, both public and private, were ordered shut down.

Some establishments with fountains which used recirculating water, cut them off in deference to public opinion.

The management of one building felt it was necessary to apologize for its pristine appearance. Their explanation was a little odd. A sign placed in a ground floor window contained the message: "No water was used in cleaning this building. We clean exclusively with steam!"

Even the number one and number two car-rental corporations, Hertz and Avis, abandoned their frantic competition long enough to agree not to wash their automobiles. Their ashtrays were clean, but their chassis were (by their own high standards) filthy.

As the drought continued unbroken, city authorities ordered all air conditioners, prodigious users of water, to be operated on a reduced basis. Office workers, shoppers and theatergoers suffered unconscionably throughout the summer. The fire department, wherever possible, began using salt water from the harbor to fight fires.

But despite everything, the level in the city's reservoirs continued to fall, and the outlook grew more and more ominous.

Finally, on the first Monday in August, rain fell throughout the watershed. But rejoicing was short-lived. In normal times, the half-inch showers would have added well over a billion gallons to the reservoirs—close to a day's supply for

23

the steaming city. But the early August downpour fell upon earth, cracked, parched and dehydrated by four water-short years. The thirsty ground soaked it up like a blotter, and only 600 million gallons finally reached the reservoirs. On that same day, even with the harsh restrictions in effect, the city used a billion gallons. The disheartening result: a net deficit for the day of 400 million gallons, in spite of the rain.

New York's chief water engineer, Edward Clark, predicted that—in the absence of drastic weather changes—the city would "run out of water by the middle of February." Another spokesman wryly observed, "It's the first time that anyone has ever prayed for a hurricane."

How had such an impasse been allowed to develop? It wasn't altogether for lack of planning. But like an outfielder who plays too close to the infield against a normally light hitter only to have the unexpected, well-hit ball sail over his head, New York water planners had discounted the possibility of a prolonged drought.

New York depends on a huge reservoir system to supply its water. As the area continued to grow and vast water storage became necessary, state and federal water experts made a detailed study of all data then available to project future needs. Of prime importance were the weather histories. Analyzing more than ninety years of such records they decided that a two-year drought was about the longest to be anticipated. Other projections as to population growth and future rates of water consumption were worked into the overall reservoir plan.

As a result of these studies, the reservoir system currently in being and under construction, has a total capacity of 572 billion gallons of fresh water. Should these lakes be filled to their brims, a 457-day supply of water would be theoretically available. A fifteen-month reserve! It sounded impressive. Unfortunately the experts missed by a wide mark, and the lack of precipitation by mid-1965 lasted twice as long as they had thought possible.

One year earlier, in the third year of the water paucity, these reservoirs already had dropped to 351 billion gallons, and by early August of 1965 they had only 212 billion gallons remaining. If the drought continued unabated, the last drop would be drained off in late December 1965 or early January 1966—in spite of the most drastic restrictions. Should it come to this, millions of New Yorkers, for all practical purposes, might almost as well be living in the Sahara Desert.

Everyone was looking for someone *else* to blame. Some castigated the city for never having installed a system of individual meters for all private residences. To do so would cost an estimated $84 million. Others, now blessed with hindsight, condemned officialdom for dismantling the Chelsea pumping station, sixty miles upriver. Installed as a sort of auxiliary "spare tire" during an earlier water scare in 1954, the Chelsea station had been later discontinued in an economy move. Opprobrium was heaped upon the useless waters of the Hudson River, which flow directly through the stricken area, but which are so badly polluted as to be wholly unsafe for human consumption.

All this took a tremendous economic toll. Swimming pools, greenhouses, water sporting goods suppliers and others found their businesses drastically affected. Some actually were forced out of business altogether. In some cases, industries were driven to purchase necessary water supplies from private sources. Swimming pool owners, having invested hundreds of thousands of dollars in their recreational facilities, now found that the going price of water from private sources was a minimum of one and a half cents per gallon—more than seventy times the usual rate.

Upstate grazing land for large herds of cattle dried up; truck farms no longer could be maintained for production of foodstuffs, and lowering water tables in rural areas forced residents to buy drinking water at the rate of fifteen cents per gallon. Recalling that in the western states during the 1950's this identical plight had lingered for seven terrible years, the farm population began to count its reserves and wonder how long it might hold on.

Irony entered the picture. The state of Oklahoma, not too long ago considered the center of America's Dust Bowl, shipped fifty-five hundred gallons of water into New York to replenish a pond in its exhibit at the New York World's Fair. Shortly thereafter, Tiffany's, that model of decorum and dignity, made news when a water fountain in its display window was converted to another liquid—eighty-four fifths of gin.

The crisis was not confined to New York. Neighbors to the south suddenly discovered an ominous development in the Delaware River Basin. The flowage rate of the Delaware dropped with alarming speed, permitting the encroachment of salt water from the Atlantic Ocean into what was normally a fresh-water area. Tests revealed that this intrusion into the estuary of the river would soon reach the intake point of Philadelphia's water supply, rendering it useless. An emergency meeting of the Delaware River Basin Commission was called.

Four states—New York, New Jersey, Pennsylvania and Delaware—comprise this body, whose purpose is to insure that every state along the river will have an equal right to its water. When this body pondered the problem, they determined that only New York City could save the water supply of Philadelphia and other nearby communities. It is the watershed of that city's supply which provides the flow that becomes the Delaware River. Since no water was flowing into the stream from the arid watershed, only those waters contained in the reservoirs of New York City could maintain even a reasonably safe flow to thwart the intrusion of the Atlantic.

The Supreme Court in 1954 had decreed that New York, in times of drought, must supply 200 millions gallons a day to insure continuous flow for the Delaware River. Mayor Robert F. Wagner had no choice but to accept the commission's decision that his city must continue this supply. However, stating that his first responsibility was to the residents of New York City, Wagner declared that he would honor this commitment only until September 10, when the eleven-year-old agreement would expire.

Thus Philadelphia and New York City, as Secretary of the Interior Stewart Udall put it, seemed set "on a collision course over the use of water." Shades of the Wild West!

New York and New Jersey, Secretary Udall said, were "walking on the edge of disaster."

Meanwhile, newspapers in Washington, D.C., in mid-June had been quoting water experts to the effect that even though the nation's capital was on the edge of the drought area, it would not suffer any real inconvenience. Suddenly these cheering predictions proved wrong and water shortage became a reality when the Potomac River suffered an alarming drop in its rate of flow. Underground supplies were being depleted; rationing of surface supplies might be in the offing. It became apparent that more than nine inches of rain would be required very soon if the area was merely to stay even. The tentacles of drought had reached out, threatening to strangle even more metropolitan areas. Topic A along the entire East Coast was no longer Vietnam, domestic race troubles or politics, but rather the most necessary and indispensable resource of all—fresh water.

The problems were not confined within the East Coast area, but the hue and cry was simply loudest from there because nearly 40 million humans for the first time in their lives were faced with this kind of crisis.

The Great Lakes, containing a fourth of the earth's supply of fresh water, continued to recede, as they have been receding for many years. But the level was falling more rapidly now. Commercial shipping was being seriously affected. The shores of Lake Erie, as an example, became noisome swamps and the water turned repulsive.

Elsewhere, record deluges plagued the West, Northwest, Missouri and Mississippi Valleys and caused serious floods. Denver, "the mile-high city," suffered a flood that cost millions of dollars in damages. Although the Colorado capital sits high up a mountain, its watershed is even higher. When heavy, gully-washing rains fell, a wall of water smashed into Denver and surrounding communities, creating unbelievable havoc and devastation. Had it not been for foresighted planning, the toll would have been astronomically higher.

Some years ago the U.S. Army Corps of Engineers constructed the Cherry Creek Reservoir and Dam above Denver. Critics had ridiculed the need and hooted at the project as a $15 million "boondoggle." The two-day deluge in June brought enough water to fill the nearly empty reservoir, but the $15 million "boondoggle" in one whack prevented more than $130 million in flood damages.

The Colorado flood had some redeeming advantages. The deluge filled the fifteen-mile-long John Martin Lake, which, since its completion in 1948, never had been anywhere near full and recently had been bone-dry. More than 358,000 acrefeet of water flowed into the cavernous void, turning the empty bowl into a depository suddenly worth $11 million, based on the current value of water in the West.

Another flood had a shattering effect on the little Texas town of Sanderson. This town, located a hundred miles west of Del Rio, near the border of Mexico, had long been accustomed to chronically inadequate rainfall. Drawing their water from underground supplies, citizens had worried for years over the rapidly declining water table. Then, one day, without warning, the heavens opened up and poured out a torrential, driving downpour which hurled a wall of water onto the town with such sudden ferocity that more than twenty human beings were washed away and drowned. Homes, businesses, vehicles, everything in the path of the torrent was pounded and destroyed. Finally, after the waters had receded, and the dead had been buried, the debris cleaned up and the rebuilding begun, it was found that the rainfall for the first time in decades had completely recharged the underground supply. Unfortunately Nature, in rectifying an intolerable situation, had exacted a terrible toll in human life and collected a multimillion-dollar fee in the process.

While some, in the summer of 1965, thus found their cups running over, a greater number found nothing but rust in theirs.

But overages and shortages were but two of the manifold facets in the water problem.

The country's streams were growing more polluted. Newspapers in every region were featuring sickening stories of the filth that bobbed along the creeks and rivers. The Cleveland *Plain Dealer* did a two-page color spread in its August 1 rotogravure section on the Cuyahoga River, which ranges at Cleveland's harbor from a rusty brown caused by the iron oxides discharged by steel plants, to a calcium-white near the gypsum mines. Nowhere is the Cuyahoga blue; nowhere is it inoffensive to the nose.

Even established communities, long served by deep-well underground sources of water, began to worry about pollution. Largely unknown to the public, health authorities throughout the country were following the study of a baffling epidemic which first broke out in late May of 1965, in Riverside, California. Death and debilitating disease lurked in the water taps of the city.

For more than seventy-five years the water supply for Riverside, currently numbering about 130,000 residents, has consisted of thirty deep wells. Never in the city's history had there been a hint of pollution or contamination. The water was sweet and pure.

Suddenly a rash of sickness broke out in Riverside over the weekend of May 22. It was blamed on food poisoning. Several dozen younger persons had been stricken with attacks of vomiting and diarrhea, coupled with extremely high temperatures. As the days went by, the epidemic escalated. Health authorities from the community, the state and the U.S. Public Health Service, went to work at breakneck speed to run down the cause. By the end of the month, the bewildered investigators had exhausted every avenue of probable source. Restaurants, food stores, suppliers and afflicted families had been thoroughly checked out in the search for a common denominator. None could be found. Still the cases mounted. The experts worked desperately, but as quietly as possible, since panic could result if the population should realize the scope of the outbreak.

Finally one specimen taken from a patient revealed the existence of *salmonella typhimurium*, a germ related to typhoid. Suspicion fell on many possible sources as to its origin, including dairy products, but the most exhaustive investigation failed to turn up a clue. As a last resort, the bacteriologists turned to the water supply. There they found the source of the epidemic. Immediately they inserted massive doses of chlorine into the city's water supply in an effort to halt the spread of the disease.

For the first time there was a drop in reported cases, which by the end of July had reached eighteen thousand. The children had suffered most. Characteristically they remained seriously ill for a week. Most adults had recovered more quickly. Three deaths, those of a five-day-old baby, a teen-age girl and a middle-aged woman suffering from cancer, were attributed to the epidemic.

To date no cause for the contamination in the water system of Riverside has been found by the investigators. No sewage or other seepage was found anywhere, no dead animals or any other foreign germ-producing matter could be located. At this writing the professionals remain baffled, although their research continues.

Fishermen and outdoor recreational enthusiasts throughout the summer of 1965 found more and more water recreational areas were denied them because of unsanitary conditions. Reports of massive fish kills in allegedly fresh waters poured into the offices of the U.S. Public Health Service. By late August, kills in excess of 100,000 fish had been officially documented on five occasions. In late July, more than 600,000 fish died in Pennsylvania's Woodcock Creek, within hours after a crop-dusting aircraft had sprayed a potato field. State officials in Iowa reported two extreme cases: Improper sewage treatment killed 200,000 fish in the North Raccoon River at Lake City, and when another 400,000 were killed in the Iowa River at Coralville, experts pointed the finger of suspicion at a nearby paper mill. A discharge of ammonia from a fertilizer plant in Fairmount, Illinois, destroyed another 100,000 in Jordan Creek.

One of the more ironic incidents took place in Chachuma Lake, Santa Barbara, California. In an attempt to eliminate algae from the water system, an excessive amount of copper sulfate was piped into the lake. Within hours the reservoir was covered with an estimated 600,000 dead fish. Almost certainly the record estimate of 18 million fish destroyed by unnatural causes in U.S. waters during 1964 was exceeded in 1965.

The water problems of the summer had their bizarre side. Some 700,000 visitors each year tour the Everglades National Park in Florida. This brooding mass of swamps, bays, vegetation and wildlife is also suffering from the alarming lack of fresh water. One inhabitant faced with possible extinction because of the intrusion of saline water is the alligator. While not exactly the sort of pet you'd want around the house, the alligator has long been considered sufficiently rare that conservation methods have been in force for decades to prevent his disappearing from our native wildlife inventory. Currently the U.S. Park Service has undertaken a SAVE OUR ALLIGATORS program. Roving teams seek out the species in badly affected areas, capturing them and removing them to these remaining areas of the Everglades where fresh water, necessary for their continued life, exists. So a new, and it is hoped temporary, occupation of "alligator social worker" has emerged.

As the summer of 1965 drew to a close, more Americans than ever before were in water trouble of one type or another. Most of the problems were not new. But they were, unmistakably, proliferating.

Their solution is not merely desirable. It is imperative. For water is not simply a commodity used to bathe children or wash dishes or float battleships. Water is life itself, and in too many places it is vanishing from our midst.

33

2 Thirsty Cities

"Thine alabaster cities gleam
Undimmed by human tears . . .
—Bates: *"America the Beautiful"*

It is a cliché to say that the face of America is changing rapidly, but, nonetheless, few people really know *how* rapidly it is changing.

Our grandfathers and our fathers grew up in a culture predominantly rural, in which land was our cheapest commodity and water was free and inexhaustible. We inherited a tradition of prodigality, because there never was any apparent reason why we should conserve our most precious natural resources.

But even before World War II, the urbanization of America had begun. Farmers began moving into the cities. The remaining farms were merged into larger and larger holdings. More and more, men who owned and worked on farms lived in nearby towns and drove out to their jobs like managers and laborers in the city.

During the two decades since the end of World War II, a real transformation took place. We have 190 million people in the United States in 1966. The Bureau of the Census tells us that two-thirds of us, or 125 million people, live in what are called "urban areas." We have become city dwellers.

The remaining one-third, or 65 million, live in "rural areas," but that does not necessarily mean that they are "down on the farm." Forty million of these are living in towns which are too small for their inhabitants to be listed as "urban." Only about 15 million people, or less than 8 per cent of our people, actually live "on the land."

As the farm population decreases, the amount of arable land decreases also. On the outskirts of every city in the United States, trees are being felled and meadows are being leveled to accommodate new housing developments, new roads leading to those housing developments, new industrial complexes, new shopping centers.

With each new development, the water balance of the nation shifts a little. The forests and meadows and fields, which used the waters naturally, also stored and conserved them. They are giving way to concrete and asphalt surfaces which throw off the water unused, and which are part and parcel of suburban or industrial developments which are themselves enormous consumers of waters that are stored elsewhere.

Where trees and native plant life once found ample succor from the rainfall, neat rows of houses now march in line behind their inevitable grass carpets. With typically more leisure time, the suburbanite waters his shrubbery, his flower beds, his lawn. The thirsty lawn grasses which have become a status symbol in American suburbia often soak up water at four and five times the pace required by the native grass and shrub life.

Today when it rains on these areas, the water does not

35

linger to sink slowly into the earth and recharge the underground supply. It runs off rapidly over the increasing miles of nonabsorbent asphalt and concrete. And on the hot pavement around the shopping centers after a summer downpour, you can both see and feel the steam rising as rainfall disappears back into the sky whence it came. Thus, our suburbs not only destroy our natural water reserves, but they also suck up existing sources of water at a frightening rate.

Washing machines with enamel-plated efficiency put the clothes and dishes through several rinsings, extravagantly squandering the domestic water supply and discharging insoluble detergent suds into the sewer lines. In any neighborhood where income level and yard-size permit, someone inevitably will build a backyard swimming pool. Soon every family will find itself under pressure to get one. As you fly by plane sometime over any reasonably affluent neighborhood in any city with fairly warm summer weather, just count the private swimming pools which throw back the sun's rays. In such neighborhoods, the loss to evaporation averages in the hundreds of thousands of gallons daily.

This is our way of life. We like it. We sweat to pay for it. And we're not about to give it up. But it gulps away at our one truly indispensable vital resource in absolutely frightening quantities.

There is no turning back. The civilization we have set in motion rolls over the land at an ever-accelerating pace. There are, altogether, 1,903,800,000 acres in the United States. Already a full one-tenth—194 million acres—strains under the weight of cities, towns and highways. This figure is increasing daily. Nearly 2 million more acres annually are absorbed into urban uses as the concrete and blacktop invasion pours across America. In the next forty years, an additional 80 million acres will be cut from woodland and pasture to make way for homes and factories to serve our mushrooming population.

Suburbia has a unique position in America's present water crisis. These new communities that have proliferated since the end of World War II represent both cause and effect in the national water problem. It is suburbia that houses our new millions, and these homes feel most the thirst of water shortage and the poison of water pollution. The indignant, uncomprehending voices of anger when water runs either dry or bad are loudest there. It is immensely ironic that the construction of suburbia is so largely accountable for that which its occupants protest.

But along much of the eastern seaboard, around the Great Lakes, down California's coastline and in spotty array along the Gulf Coast from Houston and New Orleans, a new concept in urban life is arising—the megalopolis, or super-city. As described in a Washington newspaper, "Our city of tomorrow amounts physically to a single urban community. It has many community-wide interests. Politically, however, it has no unity, no identity even. It is a formless conglomerate of independent jurisdictions, each going its own way, often conflicting with neighboring jurisdictions in the process."

It is not premature to state that the super-city or megalopolis, which we used to relate, as that newspaper did, to "tomorrow," is already here. The homes and highways of 30 million people stretch upward along the east coast from Norfolk, Virginia, to Boston. By 1980, over 50 million Americans will be clustered in this almost unbroken megalopolis. Concrete, asphalt and brick will lie in one almost seamless carpet joining Philadelphia, New York, Boston, Baltimore, Washington, Richmond and Norfolk.

Chicago, Milwaukee and South Bend will skirt the Great Lakes in one sprawling metropolitan and suburban area. San Francisco and Los Angeles will meet; San Diego will span north to join them. Dallas and Fort Worth will merge into one.

These things will happen, that is, unless these crucially impacted areas run out of water first. If that should happen, the nation would be hit by an economic collapse, the likes of which we've never seen, and from which we might never recover.

Already we are realizing that this runaway growth has far outpaced our readiness for it. The following exchange between Governor Richard J. Hughes of New Jersey and Congressman John S. Monagan of Connecticut during a recent Congressional hearing held in New Jersey points up the dilemma in which we are caught, the dilemma between our civic hunger for growth and our incapacity to deal with it:

MR. MONAGAN. . . . I am sure you are familiar with the word "Megalopolis." Flying up from Washington, particularly from Philadelphia to Trenton, we couldn't help being impressed with the fact that you are really one community all the way, and, of course, as you state, the desirability of having this interstate unit which will take into cognizance the problems of the whole area in a way that individual States or cities could not do.

Gov. HUGHES.   We rejoice in this anticipated growth. We like growth very much, but it is a little alarming in many respects, including the problems (of water supply and pollution).

"Explosive" is the term often used to describe this pattern of growth. "Atomic" might be more accurate. The tremendous chain-reactive consumption of energy and space occurring in the booming building of the suburban filler for megalopolis is overwhelming. Officials are seriously alarmed at the constant mushrooming of demand which suburbia places on existent facilities and resources. Typical is this statement given in Congressional testimony by a sanitary engineer:

The treatment methods (municipal and industrial waste disposal) themselves are not (obsolete), sir. The population is growing so fast that by the time we get the last plant built the first one will be obsolete . . . from the standpoint of overloading..

No one anticipates that the "overloading" will let up. Population projections astound even the prepared observer. The graphic lines of U.S. population charts, cautiously broken into dots and dashes—apprehensively parenthesized and labeled "estimate"—snake their way past the approaching 200 million mark and stretch upward toward a third of a billion in our lifetimes. An ever-increasing percentage of these new millions will crowd into our cities.

Where these new millions will live will be affected largely by the location of water supplies. The affluence of kings will not satisfy thirst. The dollar billions of gross national product are a reflection of the burgeoning industrial consumption of water. They could be halted in their dizzying upward

39

climb and spiral downward, just as dramatically, if we ran out of the indispensable commodity. The problem of watering the future America must be met now.

Brevard County, Florida, where Cape Kennedy is located, underscores the point. The county experienced a 571 per cent increase in population between 1950 and 1964. Our vital space installation depends on Orange County for its water supply, piped from a source forty miles distant. So does the suburban sprawl which it has set in motion. Local authorities are worried over how long the artesian wells can hold out, as the underground water table falls annually. In the fashionable new housing developments on Merritt Island at Cocoa, Florida, it is a recurrent question of feast or famine, sometimes both at once. In one recent period, floodwaters washed out and exposed the pipeline from Orlando, leaving Cape Kennedy and the housing projects temporarily without water to drink, while floods covered almost the entire flat coastal area. Backyard wells on Merritt Island, dug to the shallow depth of six feet, yield so strong an iron content that white sheets, towels and clothing are stained an unmistakable orange when washed. But if the wells go two feet deeper, they yield sulphur and, deeper than that, they produce salt.

Throughout America

This problem is not confined to any one section of the country. It is national in scope, touching municipalities in every part of the land. In the summer of 1965, I conducted a survey among the mayors, city managers and water superintendents of some three hundred American cities. A detailed questionnaire was sent to the responsible official in every U.S. town of fifty thousand or more inhabitants and to a scattering of other slightly smaller municipalities. Two hundred and sixty-eight replies were received, and this unusually high rate of return in itself indicates the dawning realization among city officials of the crucial nature of the water problem. I then talked with some of these people personally and corresponded with numerous others in considerably greater depth.

The results were astounding. Practically all of these 268 larger cities and towns throughout America have grown during the past five years. In the decade preceding the survey, 71 per cent had grown at a pace considerably faster than the rate of growth for the country as a whole.

Although only 66 of the 268 say that they already have experienced "severe" water shortages, a vast majority of them anticipate such a crisis in the foreseeable future.

While three-fourths of them report having spent considerable funds since 1960 (aggregate local water expenditures reported by this group for the past five years exceed $2.1 billion) for additions to their cities' total water capacities through new sources or additional treatment works and distribution mains, only 85 feel that these costly developments —based upon the same percentage of growth which occurred in the preceding decade—will be adequate for 1970. The other 183—or 68 per cent of the spokesmen for the larger towns—readily admit that, in spite of all they have done, their planning still will not meet their needs in five years.

One hundred and sixty-three of the 268 cities use surface supplies—rivers or lakes—for their major source of water. But the remaining 105 rely primarily on underground supplies. The water requirements for this latter group are being met basically by wells which reach into the sands below them. Somewhat startlingly, the survey reveals that most of these underground resources are playing out. Of the 97 which had undertaken studies of the underground waters, 72 replied that the subterranean water tables on which they have been drawing are lower than they were ten years ago. Twenty-seven said they were "about the same." Only six of the entire group reported an improvement in the subterranean tables over the past decade.

Mayor Louie Welch of Houston, whose booming metropolis has depended on deep-water wells for a major portion of that growing city's supply, reports that the underground source is receding at a level of eight feet every year. Mayor Perry Campbell of the smaller East Texas city of Nacogdoches, where rainfall normally exceeds that in the remainder of the state, declares that in the past ten years local water tables have fallen approximately sixty-five feet. Paul Beermann, mayor of Tucson, reports that in a seventeen-year period some wells have had to be lowered seventy additional feet to reach the water. This is hardly surprising since the population of Tucson has grown from forty-five thousand in 1950 to a quarter of a million today.

Phoenix, with 575,000 people in its municipal water service area—four times the number it had fifteen years ago—estimates that the wells which provide 35 per cent of its total supply have had to reach 120 feet deeper into the ground to find the life-giving fluid.

Green Bay and Wauwatosa, Wisconsin, both found their

wells sucking dry air and had to search out other sources, according to Mayor Don Tilleman of Green Bay, and Jack Nash, Superintendent of Wauwatosa's water department. Green Bay finally piped water from Lake Michigan, and Wauwatosa—whose population had doubled in a decade—in 1964 had to begin purchasing all its water from the city of Milwaukee.

Milwaukee, incidentally, supplies the water for eight suburban communities. This dependence on the major metropolis nearby seems to be a growing trend throughout the country. Allen Thompson, mayor of Jackson, Mississippi—whose population has grown by two-thirds in the past ten years—points out that his city joined others in creating the Pearl River Water Supply District which supplies five Mississippi counties out of a new $25 million reservoir covering thirty-two acres. Still, Mayor Thompson is dubious that this program will serve the foreseeable needs of five years hence.

Out West, in Albuquerque—where the city's population has increased 150 per cent since 1950—they experience another kind of problem resulting from suburban sprawl. Conrad Gonzalez, Albuquerque's Chief Water Engineer, declares that the thing which concerns that city's residents most is "the sewerage generated by the unorganized building and development in the county, *outside* of the corporate city limits." Gonzalez stresses that "the only sources of sewage treatment" in the various communities contiguous to Albuquerque are "private septic and cesspool systems." Continuation of this type of random development, he fears, cannot fail to pollute the underground supply from which Albuquerque draws its water. Essentially this same problem was cited by spokesmen from Miami; Spokane, Washington; and Greenville, South Carolina.

El Paso, where the average rainfall is only about seven inches a year, must get 80 per cent of its water from underground sources since the only surface water available is the Rio Grande River, and the growing city—which doubled its population in eight years—is at the mercy of the U.S. Bureau of Reclamation for allotments via the river from Elephant Butte Dam. The underlying water table fed by the sparse rainfall is not only dropping, but becoming increasingly more mineralized, according to Mayor Judson Williams.

A fast glance at a map of the United States will demonstrate both the sameness of the basic problem and the diversity of its components. High Point, North Carolina, doubled its population in the last decade, and the Director of Public Utilities says that development of additional surface storage is a must. Cincinnati's municipal water works serve an area of 850,000 people. The city has spent $34 million on improvements in the past five years, and knows that, even with the Ohio River as a continuing supply, its costly improvements will not keep pace if the population continues to grow over the next five years as it has during the past ten.

Paul Morris, Administrative Assistant to the Mayor of Cambridge, Massachusetts, points out that the water system for that historic town is more than a hundred years old. "The development of its reservoirs and water system some seventy-five years ago was made in sparsely settled areas," he explains. Today the entire complex of the formerly rural sections has been utterly transformed within the metropolitan Boston area. "Industry and housing development has occupied the watershed, preventing expansion of surface reservoirs," Morris points out, concluding that it is "imperative that water resources for larger metropolitan areas must be developed in remote regions requiring long transmission lines."

San Diego has spent $105 million since 1960 on capital water and sewer improvements. But city planners anticipate that this will be wholly inadequate by 1970. Oklahoma City, with a 70 per cent increase in population over the past several years, today transports water from a source a hundred miles away by mechanical lift stations, and Water Director Frank S. Taylor knows they will need additional capacity by 1970 in spite of an $82 million investment in these facilities. Taylor believes that lack of water has retarded Oklahoma City's economic development since the city has not been able to welcome new industries which would become huge users.

Lancaster, Pennsylvania, unlike most of the cities surveyed, has neither gained nor lost population in the past decade. Even so, and in spite of a million-dollar improvement in treatment facilities, its spokesmen realize that increasing per capita use will make the system inadequate by 1970. Pontiac, Michigan, did experience a severe water shortage but corrected it in time, and believes that it has lost no industry as a result. City Manager W. H. Carper of Raleigh, North Carolina, also reports that his community underwent a critical shortage but corrected it in time. Raleigh is in the process now of adding to its water capacity, but Carper thinks this will not be enough to last out the 1960's.

Philadelphia has spent $104 million on water and sewage works in the past five years. Its spokesmen believe its supply situation is now adequate, but report that severe problems

have been encountered in water *quality*. About half the city
has a combined sewer system carrying both sewage and storm
runoff in the same outfall lines.

Charles P. Clifton, Mayor of Ballinger, on the western
plains of Texas, casts a gloomy prognosis. Because of the increasing water shortage throughout his area, he says, "To me
it is doubtful if these towns will be around, fifty years from
now!" Across the state in the East Texas town of Palestine,
O. J. Wagner, Public Works Director, says that his city "is
fast approaching a water crisis" with underground water tables receding, and he sees the only hope for the future lying
in a sizable dam somewhere on the Neches River. Mayor
Hank Avery, of Midland, Texas, which has doubled its population three times in the past fifteen years, says his city depends on underground wells sunk into a lower water stratum
and is undergoing a "very serious" pollution problem due to
oil-field disposition of salt waters into the sands.

Cleveland, whose municipal water system serves almost
two million people—or 20 per cent of Ohio's total population
—has spent $28 million since 1960, but knows that this is not
nearly enough. Vincent DeMelto, Public Utilities Director,
points out that water intakes have been extended almost five
miles from the shoreline into Lake Erie to avoid the shore
pollution, but says in regard to the next five years that "we
must have a continuing expansion program."

St. Paul, Minnesota, citizens have just invested $41 million
in water and sewer works, but Public Utilities Commissioner
Bernard Holland thinks there won't be enough in the Upper
Mississippi headwaters to accommodate both domestic sup-

ply and recreational pursuits. He urges the Corps of Army Engineers to give priority to the former.

Roanoke, in the mountainous section of Virginia, is in the process of cutting a mile-long tunnel through the mountains to bring water to its thirsty residents, and in Colorado a $58 million project is being jointly undertaken by Aurora and Colorado Springs to bore an aqueduct five and a half miles through the Continental Divide in order to convey water from mountain lakes to the drought-suffering cities.

Sioux Falls, South Dakota, has experienced critical water shortages and anticipates more. Kansas City gets its supply from the Missouri River, but wants to reach outward for other sources. Rochester, New York, knows it must do better to avoid polluting Lake Ontario with its sewage. Conversely, Joliet, Illinois, is on the receiving end of Chicago's wastes which flow through the city via the Des Plaines River. Terre Haute, Indiana, finds its problem complicated by the 25 per cent of its residents who still use septic systems for waste disposal, and thus pollute its water sources. And little Plano, Texas—which had only 2,012 people in 1950—in 1965 is completing a plant to serve 18,500 inhabitants anticipated by 1970.

The foregoing should serve to illustrate the scope of the problem. East, west, north, south: everywhere the need is growing.

The Giants

New York City presents the most dramatic current evidence of the increasing enormity of demand on strained municipal water resources. This is the complete megalopolis, stretching as it does over into New Jersey and upward into New York State and Connecticut. New York City's municipal water system serves 7,350,000 persons in the city, and another 500,000 in surrounding suburbs. Another, smaller, system pumps for another 500,000 in Queens. Twelve hundred million gallons flow through the system daily. More than three-fourths of this must be imported through tunnels and aqueducts from sources fifty and seventy-five miles away in the Catskill mountains.

The municipal system of Los Angeles waters more than 2½ million persons by conduits from the Colorado River, hundreds of miles away, and by siphoning additional gallons from remote Owens Valley. Aqueducts swing south to supply nearly another million in San Diego.

Mayor Richard J. Daley of Chicago told a Congressional committee that the people of his city have spent millions of dollars to protect their drinking water, and to prevent pollution. Daley told the Congressmen that present needs and facilities adequately "approached" the demands of the Chicago area, but that expansion of Lake Michigan's megalopolis would call for increased action.

The pollution problems in Lake Michigan have not been completely solved. Pollution sources constantly increase from sewage and industrial wastes discharged from communities, all new, located beyond Chicago's city limits, from local discharge of sewage wastes by commercial and pleasure vessels navigating the lake off Chicago, and from frequent reverses of flow from the Chicago and Calumet Rivers during severe storms.

The southern end of Lake Michigan is befouled by the wastes from the rapidly expanding population and industrial complex in the Calumet area of Indiana. Daley said that at times, under the influence of wind-induced lake currents, slugs of these wastes have been carried for a distance of many miles to Chicago's sources of raw water serving the south side of the city. The arrival of these wastes at the intakes has at times seriously affected the bacterial quality, and caused obnoxious tastes and odors in the supply. Intensive chemical and filtration treatment are necessary to produce satisfactory water. If the pollution from the Calumet area increases materially, it will become necessary for the city to initiate action with Illinois and Indiana for tighter controls.

In the Delaware River basin, the Philadelphia branch of the East Coast megalopolis splashes in precarious shallows of supply. The whole basin is about three hundred miles long and drains an area of approximately twelve thousand square miles. It is not large, if compared to other systems, like the great Colorado or Mississippi Rivers. Even though the Delaware is not an Amazon, it is nonetheless extremely important to the nation, and especially to Pennsylvania, wherein lies 54 per cent of the basin. Twenty-two million persons, 13 per cent of the nation's population, depend on the Delaware River for everything from drinking water to recreation. And the basin's population is expected to double by the year 2000.

The Philadelphia metropolitan area, with its great industrial complex and metropolitan population of over two million, relies on the Delaware and its tributary stream, the Schuylkill River. The neighboring fertile farmland of southeastern Pennsylvania, the coal fields of east central Pennsylvania, and the Pocono Mountains resort area, although not yet welded into the Pennsylvania portion of the megalopolis, depend on the same basin.

Nowhere is megalopolis more evident than at the nation's capital. Once laid out on the banks of the Potomac to assure tranquillity and solitude for the thoughtful conduct of the nation's business, Washington was centered between the quiet, placid little river towns of Georgetown and Alexandria. Old accounts remind us that it once was a full day's trip by horseback for a resident of one of these communities to visit the other. The land reserved for the Federal District was thought fully ample to accommodate any imaginable growth. Today, alas, the District of Columbia is merely a sort of central block in a sprawling city larger than towns ever were supposed to be. It is definitely part and parcel of megalopolis.

The population of the almost square District of Columbia alone was estimated at 890,000 at the beginning of 1966 and will exceed 1,000,000 by the year 2000. As in many older communities, the vogue in established residential neighborhoods within the District is the house that grows up, not out. Thousands of houses are no more than one room wide, descending to underground basements for recreation, and stacking bedrooms in layers above the parlor. They often share common outer walls with next-door neighbors. Real estate ads tout the "semidetached" house, meaning one that is attached to an adjoining edifice only on one side.

But the congestion of the sixty-nine square miles inside the District line is merely the body of a giant municipal octopus. Suburbia climbs north into Maryland, creeping toward Baltimore, and fords the Potomac south and west, reaching deeply into Virginia. Total population in this urban and suburban complex will be almost 2½ million by early in 1966, with another million added by 1980. By the turn of the century the population may well reach 5 million.

Their water? Not too long ago the Corps of Engineers stated that the three sources for the Washington area's water supply (the Patuxent River, the Potomac River and Occoquan Creek) yielded slightly over 600 million gallons daily, at the maximum. Sprinkler irrigation has taken a substantial flow from the Potomac, by far the greatest of the three sources. The Engineers prophesied that even without irrigation the Potomac River could run dry below the Washington water intakes in 1970. The report also indicated that a serious drought could cut the flow past intakes to half the minimum requirement considerably before 1970.

Pollution and soil erosion problems add to the complexity of Washington's growing water supply headache. More than 1½ million tons of silt run off the now scraped-clean countryside along the Potomac, where the sound of building-project hammers never ceases. Almost daily, Washington newspapers feature articles on the nauseating filth that bobs to the surface of the Potomac within the shade of the Lincoln Memorial. As the megalopolis rises, and expands, the demand on the Potomac and its 9.3 million-acre watershed for clean, safe, enjoyable water gets more insistent and more impossible to fulfill.

As in every other large city, the people of the nation's capital are literally living in their own filth.

51

Twenty-Acre "Town"

There are eight bridges which connect metropolitan Washington with nearby Virginia. Four more bridges reach out to Maryland and the coast.

Every working day of the year, 150,000 Washington workers go back and forth between their homes and their jobs. For these beleaguered commuters, the suburban shopping centers are their "pit-stops" where they pause for the final time on their homeward journeys.

As we well know, many of these suburban shopping centers are enormous. Perhaps we don't quite realize how enormous they are until we explore one on foot on a blistering hot day, as I did recently.

I was thinking about water, and the concrete, steel and asphalt community gave me much to think about.

It was hot. Hot and humid. The sun beat down on the new stores and streets. Housewives and children walked close to the metal awnings, in what shade they could find. A year or so ago it had been hot too, but trees and the heavy green forest awning had absorbed the sun's fierce rays here and protected the damp forest floor. Now a black asphalt cover stretched over acres of what recently had been a meadow. White diagonal lines plotted parking places by the hundreds. The shadow of a fifteen-story apartment house, home to sixteen hundred persons, began to creep across its swimming pool, down a short hill and toward the parking lot where, by evening, it would reach all the way to the pavilion of new shops in the square of the shopping center. I reflected that this single apartment complex housed one-fourth as many people as the entire town in which I'd lived as a boy. It simply grew vertically instead of horizontally.

In the shopping center was a coin-operated laundromat. A repairman was working on a broken washing machine. Above him the simplified instructions read: PLACE SOAP AND BLEACH INTO DISPENSER AGITATOR, LOAD CLOTHES LOOSELY TO AGITATOR TOP. FOR BEST RESULTS *DON'T OVERLOAD*. INSERT COIN —PUSH SLIDE IN *SLOWLY*. MACHINE WILL WASH, RINSE, AND DAMP-DRY. PILOT LIGHT GOES OUT WHEN WASH IS COMPLETE. Then, in a colored script which weaved through a background of pictured soap bubbles and music notes: NOW RELAX— YOU'VE DONE A DAY'S WORK IN ONE HOUR!

Next to the repairman, an attendant folded clean towels. Twenty pink washers lined the wall. The repairman had torn apart the fourth one in from the window. The next three were purring through their spin cycle, and one clicked over to spray rinse, changing its dance a little. A few were standing silently, their black-top lids laid back as if in salute.

The attendant held up a colored towel and looked at it carefully. "They ever pass that stuff about soap and stuff?" she asked.

The repairman was noncommittal. He didn't know.

"They should have," she went on. "That crud keeps coming back through the water. It makes me sick."

The repairman backed out of the water and lit a cigarette with a soldering iron. "Trouble is, everybody's afraid to pass a law like that. The soap companies raise too much hell. They'd rather foul up the Potomac River than make the detergent people mad."

❋   ❋   ❋

Down the walkway, a little girl tugged at her young mother's hand, pulling toward the cashier's window and customer exit from the three-minute carwash.

"Just a minute, dear," the mother said. "I want to watch this."

The sleek new Thunderbird was rolled forward, and a workman hung a chain hook over the front bumper. The chain grew taut and the mechanical drag began to work the car through the heavy metal arches. Big beads of sweat appeared on the workman's face. He triggered off a loud steam gun used to blast the caked dirt from the car's tires and hubcaps, and wiped his face with a wet rag.

The car's bumper moved forward and tripped a lever. Two huge nylon brushes flung themselves forward and swabbed the car from each side. A hundred tiny streams of soapy water flew in every direction. The brushes whirred softly over the car's body, splashing through the misting water and working up a rich, cleansing lather. The car pushed its way through the bath and the brushes stopped.

Workers attacked the soapsuds with rinsing brushes, scrubbing off any dirt missed by the first drench. The cycle then triggered to the final rinsing, and suddenly, once more, water was everywhere, gushing out in a great stream. Just as suddenly it was over. A roar from hot-air jets burst forward, drying the dripping vehicle, and stopped. The car rolled out into the hot sun.

It had all taken only about three minutes. But it had sent twenty gallons of water down the drain.

The little girl's mother paid the cashier. She looked at the attractive plaque by the window: MEMBER AMERICAN CAR

WASHERS ASSOCIATION—INTERNATIONAL. WHICH IS DEDICATED
TO DEVELOPMENT AND ADVANCEMENT OF ALL ASPECTS OF THE
FAST CAR WASH INDUSTRY.

The cashier was talking. "Summer is the slow time. Winter
is our season. Snow and mud all over. You don't want to drive
around with a dirty car!"

The young housewife said she guessed not and left.

"Take a clean towel down to the pool when you go." The
young son answered that he would, grabbed his swim mask
from the kitchen table and went out the apartment door to
the hallway elevator without the towel.

The pool was pentagon-shaped. Young housewives lay on
deck chairs between bottles of suntain oil and soft drinks. A
lifeguard steered a long-handled net through the water, skim-
ming off bugs. A young boy received sleepy glances from
sunbathers when he splashed and squealed in the water's
shallow end.

Outside the pool's cyclone fence, mechanical lawn sprin-
klers on small tracks methodically climbed the yellow-and-
black-striped hoses, waving their sweeping showers back and
forth across brownish green grass, barely keeping it wet. A
broken coupling in the hose near the pool's cement sunning
area sprayed a hissing stream of water across three vacant
chairs and an umbrella table.

High upstairs, a curtain brushed back from inside an air-
conditioned apartment and a mother looked out and down at
the pool. When she spotted a small boy adjusting a swim
mask and plunging back into the sparkling water, she let the
curtain drop back.

*   *   *

The water was running in the kitchen. The housewife flicked a switch and a garbage-disposal unit began it guttural song. Scraps of peeled vegetables were stuffed down its throat, and the water eased the scraps away. Two ice trays came out of the freezer unit and were emptied. The disposal unit was shut off and the trays refilled under the steady reliable running tap. The door of an automatic dishwasher was lifted shut and a round disk turned. A spray of hot water could be heard. The tap was turned off. The housewife dried her hands.

These commonplace scenes took place one July afternoon last summer in suburban Shirlington, Virginia. There are hundreds of such scenes every day in shopping centers dotting Washington suburbia and the rest of the East Coast megalopolis. Thousands upon thousands of duplications occur throughout the nation, all reflecting water consumption problems that did *not exist a few short years ago*. These are new uses.

There are sixty manned "jiffy carwashes" in the Washington area. There are scores more of the do-it-yourself variety. Each vehicle which runs through the streams of the autowash is drenched with twenty gallons of water. On a busy day, an automatic carwash will run through three hundred washings. In the summer, when suburbanites wash their own cars in their backyards and front streets, the number of customers is much smaller: Between seventy-five and a hundred is probably the daily average. That averages at least a thousand gallons of water a day per establishment over the entire year.

All the automatics in the country combined use millions of gallons of water every day of the year.

The pentagon-shaped swimming pool described earlier, holds 119,000 gallons of water. This is usually drained and replaced every week. The 3,300-square-foot surface evaporates about 1,600 gallons every day. Although that particular pool is one of the larger ones, it is certainly not uniquely large for the area. Every single one of the giant apartment complexes has a similar pool, and some have two or more. And the number of private pools, now made financially accessible for thousands of budgets by cheaper construction methods and materials, is growing swiftly with each passing year.

Inside the home, the insistence on modern conveniences and time and back-saving devices has had a violent impact on domestic consumption of water. Air conditioners, automatic dishwashers, garbage disposal units and washing machines often keep the tap at "on" throughout the day.

Where suburbia is too cramped to afford all these conveniences, the coin-operated mass laundries take over. Each of the twenty pink washers spinning and rinsing through cycles in the automatic laundry where the repairman was at work uses about thirty gallons a load of wash. And each is used, according to the repairman's calculations (which check out more accurately than his philosophical musings) about five or six times a day. The coins used to operate them, when added up, substantiate that figure. If this is typical, and more than likely it is a conservative estimate, then more than three thousand gallons of water are required daily by each coin-operated center. And there are many such centers in every metropolitan area.

As I have pointed out, all these uses of water are new. A few years ago, these shopping centers were open country where water was conserved, not gulped down at the rate of thousands of gallons a minute.

To a degree, of course, our profligate consumption of water is symptomatic of our affluence. While eight million residents of New York City were using 1.2 billion gallons a day in the summer of 1965, the seven million people of London were using only 365 million gallons—less than one-third as much.

It is not really a new thing to speak with concern about the billions of gallons of water which daily run through the faucets of American homes and yards. As early as the late 1940's, some grammar school science books were asking schoolchildren, "Do you know that each time you wash your hands you will use one to two gallons of water?" and "Do you know that each time you flush the toilet, four gallons of water are used?" The soft sell didn't really make youngsters more thrifty of water. More likely, the impressive statistics merely prompted youngsters to flush the toilet for kicks, exclaiming "Wow! There goes another four gallons!"

American children take very much for granted a vast reservoir of water, not troubling their minds about whence it comes, and they become thoroughly accustomed to the idea of its on-tap availability. Although we may hear some youthful objections to its use on a washcloth behind the ears, I am sure they never once doubt its everlasting availability. Only in areas where shortage and rationing have hit is a real appreciation gained. To paraphrase an old adage, "You never value water till the well runs dry."

Where the Water Goes

Surprisingly few good studies have been made on the actual figures of domestic and municipal use of water. One of the more recent is contained in a 1961 Senate Committee report on municipal water requirements. This report indicates that on a national basis, municipal water use averages about 148 gallons per person daily, but that the figure varies region by region and river basin by river basin. In some places the per capita requirement is as high as 250 gallons. An analysis of 580 water systems supplying about 85 million persons showed that the daily use requirement is 41 per cent attributable to domestic use, 18 per cent to commercial, 24 per cent to industrial and 17 per cent to public.

A survey made in Akron, Ohio, in 1962, found that a five-member family used an average of 275 gallons of water in the home (and outside) each day. This, of course, is 55 gallons per member. The city itself then estimated that the 275 gallons washed down into these uses, based on an average daily consumption:

... 3 gallons, or 1 per cent, for washing the family car.

... 8 gallons, or 3 per cent, for watering the lawn. (A three-quarter-inch hose, under twenty pounds of pressure, discharges 400 gallons of water per hour.)

... 8 gallons, or 3 per cent, for scrubbing and cleaning the house.

... 11 gallons, or 4 per cent, for laundry uses.

... 14 gallons, or 5 per cent, for drinking water.

... 16½ gallons, or 6 per cent, for cooking and washing the dishes.

... 102 gallons, or 37 per cent, for bathing. (A typical bath is 20 gallons. A typical shower is 5 gallons a minute, using a quarter-inch pipe.)

... 113 gallons, or 41 per cent, for flushing toilets.

The total *domestic* consumption in the Akron area in 1962, based on those figures, was a little over 17 million gallons per day. This figure, incidentally, corresponds very closely with the findings in the Senate report, which estimated domestic use at 41 per cent of all municipal demand. This estimate, extracted from the reported 41 million gallons used daily in Akron, equals about 16.9 million required exclusively for domestic use. So, barring the extremely unlikely prospect that both studies might have made the same mistake somewhere, they corroborate one another. It can be concluded generally that water used in the home is very nearly half of all the water any city or urban area needs.

Total daily national water use seems to break down roughly as follows: municipal, 16.7 billion gallons; irrigation, 176.1 billion gallons (the largest diversion by far); steam, electric power, and cooling, 74.1 billion gallons daily; manufacturing, 31.9 billion gallons daily; and mining, 1.5 billion.

While municipal water, therefore, represents a relatively small part of total national consumption, it undoubtedly is the most critical phase of the problem. Scant comfort indeed to know that there are many billions of gallons flowing throughout the country if your family doesn't have enough for its needs.

An accurate perspective is seen in this statement from the 1961 Senate report:

Although of the highest priority, water demands for direct municipal use are relatively small in comparison with other uses, even when the increasing trend toward urbanization is taken into consideration.

So domestic uses are "relatively small" in comparison with other uses. Where, then, is the rub? Obvious. Water demands for direct municipal use *are of the highest priority.*" The significance of that priority is well known to any city hall official who has had to answer the screaming, justified complaints of homeowners and housewives during a local water shortage, or at a time when his community's taps spewed forth pollution or soapsuds. But the truth and validity of the priority is obvious. Individually, a single drink from the faucet at home is as important (more important, if you don't have it) as the vast power potential of the billions of gallons of liquid packed up against Boulder Dam at Lake Mead on the Nevada-Arizona border.

It may be relatively simple *statistically* to prove that an ample water supply is available for every home in the nation, but if this statistical availability is not made *functional,* and shortage results, then the problems assume crisis proportions. And the occurrence of a shortage, where anticipation, planning, and building could easily and feasibly have avoided it, is a damning indictment of our common sense.

Municipal planning has been intense, often commendably comprehensive, but unfortunately growing pains have not afforded time or space for the polish and perception which patience and careful, more measured consideration give. We can no longer afford to say, "Everything will work out in time" or "Things have a way of taking care of themselves."

61

We now have to say, "Do it now," and we must find ways to do it as swiftly and efficiently as possible.

It is painfully obvious that the position of city life in the national water picture has become crucial.

The increased drain on the capacity and capabilities of the local waterworks has reached crisis proportions. Growth does not begin to pay for itself in municipal taxes for a good many years. Many cities have strained their bonding capacity to the limit. Along with this goes, hand in hand, the problem of increased pollution of our streams, not merely from the new industrial and domestic wastes from new areas, but also from the new runoff from the concrete and asphalt watersheds of suburbia which dumps tons of silt into nearby rivers and streams. The wastes and sewage ride this runoff and the whole tide of bulk works its inexorable way, unchecked, downstream toward sister suburbia and parent megalopolis.

These individually are, on the surface, local problems, strictly municipal affairs which peculiarly affect the areas concerned. But are they merely local? Only as a mass accumulation of local shortages mounts to crisis proportions does inadequate supply become a national concern. Only as mass pollution of whole bodies of water begins to occur does pollution abatement become an impelling federal demand. But both points are being reached, rapidly.

Unless some of our proudest cities are to become ghost towns, we must act boldly—and now. It is not my desire to employ scare tactics to achieve action, because I distrust the accomplishments of frightened motion. I am not advocating a lunge for the panic button. But it should not be necessary to remind us that in speaking of water we are considering not merely a *desirable* commodity, we are speaking of the truly *necessary* ingredient without which no life is possible.

It is a straightforward proposition. The crisis is here, and presumably, in our finest tradition, we will act. The facts are the facts. If we ignore or minimize these facts we shall prove true the stark condemnation of mankind by the late Albert Schweitzer:

Man has lost the capacity to foresee and to forestall. He will end by destroying the earth.

I do not believe Dr. Schweitzer's pessimistic prognosis. But we cannot afford to be naive or complacent in a matter so vital. Dr. Schweitzer's thought must not become an epitaph for the American city.

There still is time to prevent the destruction of our cities. But not *much* time.

3 Thirsty Land

"The thirsty earth soaks up the rain,
And drinks, and gapes for drink again.
The plants suck in the earth, and are
With constant drinking fresh and fair . . ."
          —Cowley

"But the land, whither ye go to possess it,
Is a land of hills and valleys,
And drinketh water of the rain of heaven."
          —Deuteronomy XI:11

The sun bore down mercilessly on the hot plains. For days Coronado's *conquistadores,* searching for the fabled seven cities of gold, had followed the rises and falls of uncharted prairie without sighting water. Their gourds had run dry. More than once their hearts had risen as illusive heat waves had conjured mirages before their eyes—the devil's own work!—tormenting visions of deep blue "lakes" which vanished as the riders approached them.

Discipline, that stern crutch for adversity, was failing. The grumbling which is the customary lot of military men had taken a new tone—tight, constricted. The leader of the expedition knew that panic and mutiny were only hours away if they did not soon find the precious fluid of life.

64

Raising his hand to signal a halt, the captain reined in his horse and half turned, standing high in the stirrups to survey the straggling procession. He motioned the men to assemble, and slowly they brought their gasping mounts into a ragged circle. The pack burros followed, kicking up little wisps of dust in their plodding wake.

The captain was at his wit's end. There was only one thing to do. Dismounting, he asked the padre to offer a prayer for divine intervention. The troops dismounted and knelt with the priest in the dry, knee-high grass. The prayer was intoned.

It is recorded that following the fervent invocation, the horsemen returned to their saddles and followed in a direction which seemed "natural to all." Mounting the crest of a rolling hill, they saw glistening in the valley before them the waters of a broad, meandering stream.

They reached its banks in minutes. The men, sweating and exhausted, threw themselves thankfully onto the moist earth of its shoreline and drank long from its refreshing waters. The horses and burros waded deep into the river.

Their water famine abated, the soldiers indulged in ribald celebration, as men have from time immemorial when crisis is past. Their noisy whoops filled the air.

The leader of the expedition rebuked them for their lack of pious gratitude. "We have been saved," he said, "by *los Brazos de Dios*."

Los Brazos de Dios—the arms of God. For years this long, twisting stream which winds its way from northwest Texas to the Gulf of Mexico was known as El Rio de Los Brazos de Dios. Cartographers wrote it so on all the early maps of

Texas. Today, after the manner of the prosaic Anglo-Saxon, the name has been shortened. It is known now simply as the Brazos River.

In the centuries that were to follow, the sparse rivers and natural lakes that hid themselves in the rolling plains of the West surely must have seemed to the thirsty wagon trains, and to the stockmen and farmers that followed them, to be no less than the arms of God. Without them, survival would have been impossible on the prairies that stretched like a never-ending sea from the jumping-off place of civilization to the Pacific Ocean itself.

In the West, water is life. It always has been so.

The scene changes. The farmlands of Nebraska have been occupied by the hardy army of hopeful farmers who tried to wrest a living in the early 1930's from its dry soil.

A Model T banged down a dusty road toward an isolated farmhouse. Its two occupants did not speak. Both looked apprehensively ahead. The driver took an already wet bandanna from the back pocket of his threadbare business suit and wiped his damp brow. The other, dressed in work clothes, picked with an old cornstalk at the caked mud on his boots. The car pulled into the farmyard. The driver cut the spark lever and killed the engine. He sighed. Some chickens cackled toward the barn.

"Well, Warren," the driver said. "Let's see what she's got to say this time!"

A rifle shot rang across the hot silence. Instantaneously, both men toppled down and out on the safe side of their car.

On the farmhouse porch, a woman with a rifle shook her fist and yelled at them.

"Damn you, Roy Franklin," she hollered. "You git your man and hit outa here and take them irrigation contracts with you! We ain'ta buying your stolen water! God put that water in that river. If'n He wants us to have it, He'll send it *His* way!"

From beneath the old car, irrigation subscription contracts tucked in his pocket, the president of the newly formed and doing-badly Tri-County Irrigation Company, unable to see the woman, yelled back as loud as he could, "You crazy old coot, Mrs. Bradley! God put that water in the river and said, 'If you want it, you lazy critters, you come and get it!' "

It is safe to assume that Mrs. Bradley intentionally fired high the first time. She did not fire again. But her anger was genuine. This event, related to me by a friend, is representative of the countless cases of violence and foolishness which plagued so many early efforts to bring irrigation to the drying farmlands of the West and Midwest.

Farsighted men who would not sit by and watch their farms and towns dry up and blow away, began throwing canals and drainage ditches into the sides of their great rivers and sinking deep wells into the stingy soil wherever efficacious, siphoning off the life-giving waters which soon turned brown valleys green and made small towns grow large. But they had their opposition. The element of superstitious fear that often has attempted to thwart plans to control and manipulate nature, motivated many Mrs. Bradleys. Nevertheless, the patchwork of irrigation canals that water the thirsting lands of the nation began to grow until many billions of gallons daily were diverted from surface and subsurface to cause the food and fibre supply of a nation to grow.

Of course, irrigation is not a new thing peculiar to our century. It is a use of water as old as man. The second chapter of Genesis tells us: "And a river went out of Eden to water the garden: and from thence it was parted, and became into four heads." Every successful, lasting agricultural civilization developed some means of storing and distributing its waters. But in the United States during this century irrigation has really become big business. In 1909, for example, the West had a mere eight thousand acres of irrigated cotton. Forty years later, the figure was 2½ *million* acres.

Irrigation today is by far the most prodigious consumer of our national water reserves. Of the slightly more than 300 billion gallons drawn daily from national streamflow in 1954, more than 176 billion gallons, or about 60 per cent, passed through the nation's irrigation ditches to the fields of our cropland—mostly, of course, in the West and Midwest. But more astounding is the fact that net *consumptive* use figures, or those gallons *not returned* to streamflow, totaled 109.5 billion gallons in the United States, and irrigation accounted for 103.5 billion, or 95 *per cent of the total*. This means that, when water is used for irrigation, we don't get an identifiable chance to reuse it. Its product, of course—agricultural goods —is the stuff that keeps us alive.

Irrigation has brought vast changes to the face of the continent. If you fly over the long stretches of toast-brown prairies which lie like a carpet over the western half of the United States, you can spot the works of irrigation in the green, gardenlike oases that punctuate the bleak and barren expanse.

As the waters running through irrigation ditches reclaim much of the hitherto forgotten land of America, however, traditional farmlands in areas where the rainfall once was relied upon to produce the crops are turning to pasture, and pastures unwatered and overgrazed, have turned to desert.

During the past thirty years, 14 million acres of badlands have been claimed for cultivating, but in the process 48 million acres which formerly grew crops for the nation, have been retired from the cultivator's blade. This represents a withdrawal from crop harvesting of some seventy-five thousand square miles, a total area larger than the state of Oklahoma.

The story of cotton is fairly typical of what has happened to American agriculture, generally. Old cotton lands throughout the Southeast have gone to pasture while barren buffalo meadows of the West, now watered by man-made canals, grow the cotton. During the past decade, approximately 4 million acres of old cotton lands have been retired. It takes fewer acres to produce cotton under irrigation, and a premium quality of cotton results.

Before the Second World War, only about one-fifth of the nation's cotton crop came from the irrigated lands of Texas, New Mexico, Oklahoma, Arizona and California. By 1954, they were producing half the national output. In the westernmost part of this region—California, Arizona, and New Mexico, actual production has nearly doubled in the fifteen years since 1950, from 1,639,000 bales to nearly 3 million bales a year. During the same period throughout the nation the total land area given over to growing cotton has declined by some 4.5 million acres.

Texas and California are now the largest cotton-producing states in the nation, by far. So much for the traditional, romantic concept of Dixie.

In the southern delta region alone, cotton cultivation dropped from 7.3 million acres in 1951 to only 4.1 million in 1965. The old southeastern states of the Confederacy—Virginia, North and South Carolina, Georgia, Florida and Alabama—where cotton reigned as undisputed economic king in the antebellum and Reconstruction days, lost more than half their cotton lands in this fourteen-year period. In 1951, they had 29.3 million acres growing cotton. By 1965, this figure had shrunk to only 14.2 million acres.

Billie Sol Estes was violating no law—but probably transgressing the *spirit* of the nation's patchwork acreage allotment program—when he bought acreage rights from Arkansas cotton farmers and transferred those acreages to the verdant plains of the Pecos Valley where, because of irrigation, he could produce twice as much as he would have been able to produce in the eroded and largely burnt-out fields of Arkansas. He also was making himself a tidy fortune in the process.

Two serious questions arise from this westward march of cotton: What is happening to the abandoned lands in the East? And what is happening to the long-term water supplies in the West where irrigation is practiced in its most profligate forms?

The first question is answered by the statistics. Throughout the southeastern curvature of the North American continent which sweeps from Virginia's Atlantic shoreline into the eastern half of Texas, the acreage of cultivated lands devoted to agricultural harvest has fallen in three decades from about

138 million to approximately 107 million. A good part of the converted 29 million acres is given over now to grazing for livestock. It is now in the second stage of the historic cycle: from crop cultivation, to pasture, to overgrazing, to desert.

Presumably we are wise enough and prudent enough to avoid entering the third stage—overgrazing. Let us hope so.

But history holds stark lessons of other civilizations which found—too late—that they could not halt the cycle. There is much evidence to suggest that the civilizations which flourished along the Tigris and Euphrates valleys shriveled and finally perished because of their waning water supply. Much of Iraq and Iran, now desert, once provided lush pasture for the flocks and herds of ancient Persia. Throughout history, wars have been fought and freedoms surrendered when the slender patrimony of a ravaged land no longer could sustain its people.

On the Yucatan Peninsula, archeologists have unearthed evidence of the great Mayan civilization which prospered for about fourteen hundred years and reached its full cultural stride about 1000 A.D. The Mayas, however, were already in decline before the Spaniards came. Magnificent ruins of temples reveal that the Mayas were far more advanced intellectually than were most of their contemporaries. They had a 365-day calendar, for instance, when most European peoples were having trouble making sense out of the wanings and waxings of the moon. They built altars in their central city, erected a huge sports stadium, and constructed of enduring stone an enormous forum or central meeting place.

The Mayas also cultivated land. They built their civilization basically on corn, and they grazed livestock. But the land wore out, and they were at least wise enough to move on and establish their center of operations elsewhere. Several cities of Mayan ruins throughout Central America testify to the depletion of their basic resources. The Mayan nation would live awhile in one locality, allowing the land and water supply to rest and reseed itself in the regions of their old habitations, then return, after a generation or so, to take them up again. But the epitaph of their culture may be written in a sentence: The Mayan lands ran out of moisture and returned to brush.

The early civilization of Sumeria, a pastoral society which matured about six thousand years ago in the Tigris and Euphrates valleys, knew the importance of controlled land and water to human prosperity. Sumerians built an intricate network of irrigation canals and sewers. They terraced fields and harvested rich crops, thus providing themselves an early affluence which allowed time for cultural and intellectual achievement. The Bible tells of the rich silt deposits which gave life to the Sumerian society.

The Babylonians followed the Sumerians. Their leaders levied taxes which enabled them to build more extensive irrigation canals. Penal sanctions were applied against any who failed to maintain the dikes, canals and levees. The hanging gardens of Babylon became one of the seven wonders of the ancient world.

But when the Turkish hordes of nomads swept down from the north, the Babylonian dikes were destroyed. The rivers turned to raging, uncontrolled demons which drowned the rich, fertile lowlands and left the high fields without moisture. Pillage, disease and overgrazing turned the proud civilization into a broken land. The marauders moved on. And without the controlled use of the river, Babylon turned again to desert.

The Romans were wise enough to learn from the nations they conquered. They acquired the methods of water control and irrigation which centuries of necessity had taught to the civilizations of the arid Middle East and Africa. The Romans built aqueducts, dug wells and constructed reservoirs and waterworks. With typical Roman emphasis on the practical, Frontinus, the historian, wrote: "With such an array of indispensable structures carrying so many waters, compare, if you will, the idle Pyramids or the useless, though famous, works of the Greeks."

As Rome declined so did her social concern over water supplies and other public works. The depredations of the Vandal hordes completed their ruin. Water supplies became polluted and undrinkable. Silt filled the canals, and broken aqueducts marked the crumbling remains of the once efficient water-transport systems. There were many reasons, as any historian knows, for the decline of the Empire. But it is not farfetched in this connection to emphasize that Rome all but dried out.

In the fifth century, the Indian city of Pataliputra flourished along the tributaries of the Ganges. Under the rule of the Guptas, the remarkable Girnar dam had been constructed, providing the basic dynamics for a prospering civilization. When the Guptas' reign was broken, the dam was destroyed. Silt and earth filled the streets and the city was literally buried in waste. Today archeologists dig in its ruins beneath almost twenty feet of soil.

Considerably closer to home, during the period of Mayan

decline, a group of several tribes, offshoots of the Basket-weavers, settled in what is now New Mexico. They came to be known as the Pueblos. Their civilization advanced under a very liberal form of primitive democracy. Living in somewhat communal villages, they had no high priest as such and recognized no lineal birth rights to leadership. Their homes were adobe and rock structures, some of them several stories high. Such a village can be seen today, where a tribe still lives much as it did then, in Taos, New Mexico.

The Pueblos were peaceful. If theirs was not a great civilization, it was at least a good society. Lacking the nomadic tendencies of most North American Indians, they stuck to their villages, cultivating grain and foodstuffs in the surrounding lands. They even developed rude prototypes of irrigation. Throughout most of the thirteenth century, they were sufficiently numerous and well organized to repel successfully the periodic aggressive forays of hostile groups from the north. The Pueblos prospered and grew in number, and life was good.

Their communities were sufficiently impressive to be mistaken for the seven cities of gold which Coronado had sought in vain. A combination of New Mexico sun and adobe had created an illusion which had led to the legend of golden cities.

In 1276 began an occurrence which was to spell their doom. It was the first year of a drought, the beginning of a devastating, tenacious parching of the land which was to last for twenty-three years. Tree rings provide mute testimony to the succeeding years of meager rainfall which would not be relieved until 1299. New Yorkers in the grip of a four-year

arid cycle might ponder upon the unpredictable vagaries of
nature. It well may be wondered how many cities could hold
on under such prolonged punishment as the Pueblos sus-
tained for year after scorching year.

As food and water supplies no longer could support the
population, the society began fragmenting. Small groups
would leave the villages and drift away, seeking some place
where water was available and life more tolerable. Throughout two decades the exodus continued. The villages were bled
of their youngest and strongest men and their most adven-
turous families. Finally only the oldest and stubbornest and
the lame and sick were left when the savage Apaches and
Navajos swept down from the north to destroy the remaining
vestiges of Pueblo culture. But the conquest was hollow and
the plunder sparse. It was almost like robbing a grave. The
Pueblo cities already had died.

The cliff-dwelling Indians regrouped and rebuilt less pre-
tentious communities in the Rio Grande Valley. However,
the long drought had evidently destroyed their religion. The
rebuilt cities had no *kivas* for religious ceremonies. They had
lost faith in their gods.

In India, just a few hours' drive south of Delhi, there is the
fascinating, mummified city of Fatehpur-Sikri, built in the
sixteenth century by the Mogul Emperor, Akbar. It remains
almost exactly as it was four hundred years ago, a magnifi-
cently constructed community of sandstone and marble structures, a treasure house of Persian architecture at its best. (In
one courtyard there is even a painted giant parcheesi board,
on which Akbar played, using slave girls as pieces.) The city
is quite empty. It had been fed by pipes from a nearby reser-

voir, and, suddenly, one year, the water gave out. Akbar and his court deserted Fatehpur-Sikri, and the city remains, a sermon in stone, proving that man cannot live by art alone. Or, for that matter, by parcheesi, either.

The classic example comes from Shelley, who tells us of the statue of the tyrant Ozymandias, standing crumbling in the desert, with its boastful inscription: "Look on my works, ye mighty, and despair." Even for Ozymandias, the water ran out:

> Round the decay
> Of that colossal wreck, boundless and bare,
> The lone and level sands stretch far away.

Drought is the greatest of all levelers. Today, in America, the motorist traveling along highways of the West can witness in countless square miles of mesquite groves a tragic modern reenactment of these historic dramas. The mesquite yields a whiskered berry which cannot reseed if it falls on grass. Only where the surface has been denuded through rapacious overgrazing, or dwindling rainfall, will the mesquite tree grow. Chronicles of the West, some written as recently as fifty years ago, tell of native bison growing fat in waist-high waves of grasses on the very land where today nothing will take root but the dwarfy mesquite.

County Judge Scott Bailey of Eastland, Texas, has made a study of the mesquite. The runty tree, he explains, today either occupies or threatens to take over some 55 million acres of ranch land in the state of Texas alone. It was not always so.

It is certain that there was little mesquite in the Southwest before intensive grazing and herding of livestock began. The mesquite bean, rich in sugar content, was a delicious morsel for the bison that roamed the countryside. Early accounts indicate that mesquite trees existed primarily around the buffalo wallows. Those were the places to which the bison repeatedly returned to lie and roll, rubbing their shaggy hides against the ground, killing out the native grass cover. The American buffalo apparently had choice spots for this activity, and to these they would migrate again and again until the entire resting areas would become depressed and recessed like saucers and often would hold large pools of shallow water after the rains.

As I have pointed out, the mesquite bean, when dropped upon the native grassy turf, will not take root and grow. But where the bison assembled and stood for hours at a time, as they were stamping out the native grass, they were at the same time depositing the digested or undigested mesquite bean on these exposed areas of the terrain. After the beans sprouted and began to grow, mesquite thickets appeared around these scattered watering places of the buffalo. But so widely separated were the thickets that they made very little impression on the vast expanse of soil and turf.

The exodus of the bison and the appearance of the cowman and sheep and goat herders brought on the severe intrusion of the damaging shrub. As the range was overgrazed, bare and denuded surfaces of earth would furnish ever-spreading splotches of fertile ground for the whiskered bean to begin its growth.

In 1953, Bob Westerman, a rancher in Dickens County near Spur, Texas, recalled that when he came to this flat country in the late 1920's there were scarcely any mesquite at all. A man on horseback, he remembered, could see a cow grazing anywhere on a level section (640 acres) of land. At the time he made this observation in 1953, the mesquite was so solid across his land that it was impossible to see more than a few yards of earth in any direction. This has happened in just one generation.

And this is happening to maybe 100 million acres of the West.

True, mesquite and erosion do not yet dominate the agricultural life of the West. While the southwestern states retired approximately 19 per cent of all their farming lands during the dry years from 1949 to 1959, the crops were being grown elsewhere—often on irrigated land.

In the United States today, more than 30 million acres of land are watered by irrigation facilities. A full 28 million of these acres lie in the seventeen western states, where the practice is essential if the land is to yield at all. The other thirty-eight states have only slightly over 2 million acres under irrigation. However, the heavy western use of water for irrigation has a real impact on the long-term western supply and on the water policies of the entire nation.

Productive farmlands are necessary to a self-sustaining nation. While it may be popular in some quarters to decry farm surpluses (and ours is the only civilization in all history to consider the production of *too much* food a *problem*), nobody wants the reverse, food shortage. We would do well to look again at the alarming statistics of our population growth. An agricultural subcommittee of the Congress has forecast that within fifteen years we shall need the productive equivalent of 116 million *more* acres than we now have under cultivation if we are merely to feed our own people.

No statistical calculation of future food requirements and production, of course, can have any high degree of accuracy. Nobody knows what future science can contribute to increasing the yield of our lands per acre. But we *do* know that we're going to have more people. And more people must have more food. The direction which total productive acreage must take, therefore, is up. Medium-range population assumptions indicate that, in order to feed our own people, total irrigated acreages in the United States—now 30 million —should be more than 36 million by 1980 and more than 55 million by the year 2000. This represents very nearly a doubling of all irrigation use from 1954 to the start of the next century. We shall have to have the water, certainly, to enable the agriculture of the nation to feed the yet unborn millions. The wells and ditches we'll need for the future must be planned now and calculated into the master program of our future water needs. We must not wait until we couple water shortage with food shortage, each increasing the terror of the other.

In the next thirty-five years, the part that irrigation plays as a *percentage* of total national gross withdrawals from streamflow is expected to drop, even with more irrigated lands. Today it comprises 60 per cent of the total amount taken annually from our water inventory. By the year 2000, both manufacturing and the catchall category listed as "steam, electric power, and cooling" will surpass the gallon totals of irrigation. Although we will be using 8 billion gallons more each day to water our crops, the total withdrawals for irrigation will represent only about 20 per cent—rather than

60 per cent—of all withdrawals. Industrial and power uses will increase, respectively, twofold and sixfold.

But power, steam and cooling uses will return to stream-flow 427 billion gallons of the 430 which they will take out in each twenty-four-hour period. Of that amount diverted to artificially watered croplands, however, only 58 billion gallons of the 185 billion siphoned daily from the supply channels will find their way home to the river.

So, since water spread over soil does not return rapidly, the expected net daily *consumptive* use total for irrigation at the beginning of the next century—126 billion gallons—remains clearly the lion's share of all stream depletions; 80 per cent, in fact. Although this is a drop from 1954's 95 per cent depletion figure, irrigation still will be, by far, the greatest single factor in total water consumption. The 15 per cent drop is replaced by an expected increase in consumptive use by industry; a greater daily consumption, by 18 billion gallons, in the second half of the twentieth century.

This *consumptive* use of water by irrigation has a couple of other important aspects in terms both of our national water supply, and of the continued viability of the very lands it serves. Besides just not returning to the streamflow for reuse, the *chemical quality* of the water decreases steadily as it is successively used with a given irrigation project. This occurs because of continual leaching of salts as the water passes through and over the land from one field to the next. The 40 per cent, or 72 billion gallons a day, which do find their way back to streamflow, tend to exert a detrimental effect on the quality of water generally due to this salty mineral acquisition. Expected increases in the total volume of irrigation supposedly will increase this tendency. Hopefully, the threat may be partially offset by more efficient means of transmitting water and closer control of applied water to prevent irrigation waste. At least the Bureau of Reclamation thinks so. In 1959, the Bureau stated:

In closed ground-water basins, where a significant portion of recharge to an aquifer is derived from irrigation water pumped from the aquifer, the chemical or mineral content of the water may eventually be materially increased. As in the case of reused surface water, control of transmission losses and water application so as to keep recirculation of water to a minimum will be effective in reducing the deterioration of ground-water quality.

Whatever that means exactly, there *are* ways of reducing the harmful saline content of irrigation waters. But these treatments cost money—just as it costs money to convert seawater, and just as it costs money to install an irrigation system in the first place.

There can be no doubt that irrigation discharges, having run through successive fields, often do dump crop-destructive salt on the lands into which they ultimately spill. The anguish of the final receiver in such a process can be very real indeed. It doesn't much matter if the mineral-laden water finally comes to rest on unused lands, to sink slowly back into the earth. But what if it comes, after miles of leaching, to deposit its burden of harmful minerals upon the soil of an ultimate *customer* who has paid dearly for the privilege of getting this water?

As we have noted previously, just such a situation as this threatened recently to provoke an international crisis. The Mexican government had entered into an official agreement with us to allow Colorado River waters to flow into Mexico through the Morelos Dam for agricultural uses in the Mexican territory of Baja California. This right was granted in the International Water Treaty of 1944.

The trouble began in the winter of 1961–62, when Mexican scientists discovered that the saline index of the water had risen to about four thousand parts per million. Real harm resulted to the cotton and wheat crops in the rich Mexicali Valley, and large expanses of Mexico's best agricultural cropland were spoiled. The official protest of a group of twenty-four Mexican lawmakers who met with a like number from the U.S. Congress used the word "poisoning" and "progressive contamination." Considering the facts, I think their terminology was restrained and their demands not unreasonable. Clearly we *had* done injury to our southern neighbors.

It turns out that a group of irrigating farmers in the Wellton-Mohawk Valley of Arizona had been pumping heavily salted waters from their underground water basin and draining them into the bed of the Colorado River, thus contaminating the supply destined for our neighbors south of the border.

After two years of polite though pointed Congressional confrontations on the subject, and meetings of Mexican President Adolfo López Mateos with both Presidents Kennedy and Johnson, we finally devised a workable scheme for protecting the waters from this damaging saline intrusion. But it cost us several millions of dollars and, for a time, tarnished our relations.

Similarly, we discovered Mexican practices of a like nature which were discharging salt into the Rio Grande above Falcon Dam on the Texas border, and the Mexicans agreed to put a stop to that.

A heated battle in Congress developed among California members in 1964 over a Bureau of Reclamation project. The disagreement involved the question of where the waters, after serving their purpose, ultimately were to be dumped; whether onto other farmlands or into San Francisco Bay. Ironically, as valuable as water is, nobody wanted *this* water after it had passed over and through so many lands and gathered so many undesired minerals.

But damaging mineral content is not the only problem associated with heavy irrigation. Another is the basic question of continued *supply*.

Irrigation has reclaimed many of the arid acres of the sagebrush and dry sands country, and has put them into bloom. Long-staple cotton and vegetables flourish abundantly where once the unwatered wastelands grew only cacti, prickly pear and horned lizards. It is, in short, a worker of miracles. But there is a limit to the amount of water which can be brought to surface in a given area. Underground water tables are not inexhaustible.

In the entire thirteen-county South Plains area of West Texas, for example, there were not more than two thousand water wells only two decades ago. Today, more than thirty thousand wells puncture the landscape to leach the underground waters for the profitable cotton crops. These counties, incidentally, account for approximately one-fourth of the nation's total cotton production today. But subterranean waters are receding. Just as regularly withdrawing more funds from the bank than we deposit will inevitably result in an overdraft, so can the practices of overirrigation ultimately impoverish the treasure house of underground streams.

The farmers on the South Plains have known for years that the days of their prosperity could be numbered. They have tried, to the degree that modern knowledge and limited resources permit, to take care of the underground water tables.

In an effort to re-collect the irrigation waters and trap the inadequate rainfall, and thus "pay back" the subterranean storehouse, they've constructed thousands of shallow ponds in the sandy loam throughout the region. Here the waters from their gently sloping fields run together and collect. Gradually, through the pond's porous bed, the waters sink into the earth again—through the topsoil and the subsoil and into the river sands that feed the wells.

It may not sound very scientific, but it does help. Through this device, the farming population undoubtedly has added years to the life expectancy of the underground streams which are the very lifeblood of the region's entire economy.

Even so, massive irrigation from wells saps the subterranean waters more rapidly than they can be replenished. It is significant that of seventy municipalities recently surveyed in areas of heavy irrigation, sixty-two reported an appreciable decline in the underground water tables.

This could mean very serious trouble in the foreseeable future.

If it should reach the point where present demands for irrigation can no longer be met, men may be led to bitter controversy, or worse. The old water-hole feuds of western frontier cattle empires could be revived in all their drama and agony. It is hoped it will not come to this. Proper conservation programs, plus decent restraint and common sense, may eventually prevail. But the ingredients—a hungering population which pays well to be fed, a dropping river level, receding underground water tables, a limited flow through irrigation channels to the farmer's croplands—add up to a potentially explosive situation.

It is probably true that water, or the lack of it, has precipitated more wars, more lawsuits, more fights and more feuds than any other element in history (unless perhaps, it be sex). The story of the West is replete with incidents.

The Ditchrider

This is a personal experience told to me by an elderly farmer who had grown up with the West:

A rider sharply flicked the tail end of his rein against his horse's flank, and the animal lunged up to the top of a green bank. Below muddy water flowed rapidly over a crude dam and wooden spillway. Large planks lay beside a narrow, deep ditch leading away from the main stream. Two such wooden beams, only recently removed from the makeshift spillway, lay wet in the long grass.

The rider brought his horse to a stop. A few feet away stood a glaring farmer, his hands extended and resting on a muddy shovel, his lips pursed.

"Henry," the rider said, "you got two good heads of water coming through that fall. Record says you paid for one. You take them planks out?"

The farmer spat in the dry dust at the edge of his cornfield.

"Suppose'n I did," he replied quietly.

"Suppose'n you did, means I have to put 'em back in. One head. No more." The rider started to swing his leg over his saddle and dismount.

"Hold on a minute, Mr. High'n Mighty Ditchrider!" the farmer excitedly shouted. "Look at them cornstalks out there. My whole field'll be drier'n a dead milk cow come weekend without them two heads of water! You put them boards back in, an' I'll take this shovel to ya!"

"The boards go in, Henry. Long as I been ridin' this ditch, you never caused no trouble. Don't start now."

As the rider's feet touched the ground, the shovel made a menacing arc through the dry, hot air. The rider dove for the farmer's feet, and the blade of the shovel smacked against the horse's belly below the muddy saddle-blanket. The animal gave a shrill whinny of pain and reared up on its hind legs. Farmer and rider went down in the dirt, flailing punches at each other. Braying, the horse ran out into the field and kept running.

Fights like this were common in a ditchrider's day's work. A little ashamed, my farmer friend admitted that it all had ended about as soon as it started. He recalled that he even retrieved the rider's horse while the ditchrider put the two planks back into the spillway, cutting the irrigating flow to the cornfield back down to one head. The two men involved were distant cousins and lifelong friends. But the combination of heat and drought and thirsting lands often made for short tempers. When a disagreement involved the question of who would receive how much water, violence was commonplace.

Ditchriders still exist. Pickup trucks have replaced the

horse, and two-way radios substitute for smoke signals, which the riders once used to send messages down the line; a means of communication learned, of course, from the Indians. But the ditchrider's job of surveying the flow from irrigation canals to the farms they water, of keeping the channels free from weeds and trash and of maintaining proper water levels continues. When the river runs low, so must the main irrigation canals, and so must each man's ditch. And when water runs low, tempers run high.

The ditchrider is symbolic in many ways of the roles now assumed by the various levels of government in our ever more complex society.

A brief recently filed in the United States Supreme Court by the Attorney General of Nebraska stated: "The aggressive policies of the State of Iowa have caused great consternation to the State of Nebraska and its citizens, and have threatened to result in armed conflict on the part of landowners and the State of Iowa and its representatives." Although the advocacy of the Nebraska Attorney General necessarily could not admit it, "great consternation" was also felt by Iowa citizens as result of Nebraska's attitude in this 1964 border water dispute.

The meandering Missouri River was the actual culprit in the conflict, but who can get any satisfaction out of venting his wrath on a river? Well, perhaps the Army Corps of Engineers might, and it was they who managed to stay and somewhat stabilize the bank-and-channel straying Missouri. The trained Missouri then left attractive island lands attached to the Iowa side. These previously had been claimed by Nebraskans, as Nebraska law gives riparian ownership up to the

middle of the stream. Iowa law, however, recognizes possession only to the high-water mark, and as a result, Iowans had
ignored the island lands, and Nebraskans had claimed them.
But when the river made its final shift, the Army Engineers
made the channels permanent, and about fifteen thousand
acres of Nebraska land, in twenty-nine different pieces, lay
on the Iowa side.

The Iowa Conservation Commission then claimed the land
for Iowa game and park reserves. An Iowa game warden, out
inspecting the newly acquired state possessions, was met
with rifle fire from the former landowner. Although the shots
failed to find a target (if indeed one was sought), the game
warden demanded state protective action before he would
return. The New York *Times,* reporting the incident and the
Nebraska Supreme Court brief, headlined, somewhat tongue-
in-cheek: IOWA IS CALLED AGGRESSOR STATE; NEBRASKA FEARS
SHOOTING WAR. This may not be an accurate reading of the
Nebraska Attorney General's brief, but it must surely be in
tune with the Iowa game warden's sentiments.

The issues at stake have been more profound when one
state or community or body of men has felt that another, upstream, was spoliating the water which gives life to their community or denying its flow by impoundments or diversions or
unreasonable withdrawals. Where rifles once settled such disputes, the law courts, in recent times, have become the common resort. And the number of cases involving litigation over
water increases steadily.

The cities of New York, Chicago and Philadelphia have
sued and been sued.

The trend in recent years has been for states to try to reach accommodations in matters of water use through interstate compacts. The United States Supreme Court, in 1943, expressly encouraged this method of settlement. The Court's recommendation was due in no small measure to the proliferating volume of interstate disputes which it was being importuned to resolve. Those cases were unbelievably tedious; trial master-reports were complicated and lengthy; parties to the proceedings often were numerous. But still, where formal compact and voluntary cooperation break down, the Court is called upon.

When this does happen, neighbor states sometimes are not so neighborly. With water rights and supplies at stake, legal clashes can evoke emotion as well as rhetoric, heat as well as light. Wyoming and Colorado have had it out, as has Colorado with neighboring Kansas. Washington and Oregon went to the mat legally. So did Arizona against California, New York against New Jersey, and Connecticut against Massachusetts.

In a 1928 case among states bordering the Great Lakes, Wisconsin, Michigan and New York ganged up on Illinois and the Chicago Sanitary Department, seeking an injunction to prohibit the wholesale drainage of water from Lake Michigan. The Sanitary District which operated a canal connected to the Mississippi River, sent great volumes of untreated sewage from Chicago to the Mississippi watershed, flushing it along its way with a voluminous drain-off from the Great Lakes.

Although the Secretary of War had allowed the practice by official permit, Chief Justice Taft and his associates put a stop to the drain-off. The Supreme Court, granting Chicago time to find some other means of sewage disposal, ruled that the Secretary had no authority to grant a special permit authorizing Chicago to lower the Great Lakes chain miles away. The case took no less than thirty-two lawyers in Supreme Court argument, numbering among them the Attorneys General of ten states, including faraway Louisiana.

When the Supreme Court indicated, in 1943, that it would like to see resolution of interstate problems through compacts, it had before it a suit against Kansas by Colorado involving the Arkansas River waters. Colorado had sought to enjoin Kansas interests from any further litigation against water users in Colorado. For years, Coloradans had been plagued by subpoenas from Kansas. The Jayhawk state seized upon the opportunity to ask for a decree, relying on the equity of her downstream position, entitling her to all the water she desired, not only from the Arkansas but from Colorado rivers as well. But Kansans evidently bit off more than they could chew. They lost on all major counts, in a legal battle which actually had begun in 1901, forty-two years earlier.

Southern California's municipalities seem almost always locked in a legal combat over one water case or another. A battle that began with the organization of the Coronado Water Company in 1886 found its way to the higher appeals court of California in 1941. The final trial was between the City of Coronado, and the City of San Diego, involving a 1912 contract which obligated San Diego to sell and deliver water to Coronado.

This wasn't the first water fight for San Diego. In 1930, the town won a six-year-old case against a waterworks on the theory that modern San Diego, as successor to the pueblo of

San Diego, had prior and paramount right to the waters of the San Diego River in order to satisfy its municipal requirements. The precedent was an earlier decision granting similar pueblo rights to Los Angeles.

Glendale had sued Los Angeles in a dispute involving the Los Angeles River. Because the citizens of sprawling Los Angeles depended on the water supply in the San Fernando Valley, the court ceded them a prior right, through succession from the old pueblo rights, to all the water in the basin.

Legal problems concerning water are common among private citizens as well as among cities and states. Judicial records are replete with disagreements among neighbors in almost every sector of the land over the commodity of water. Sometimes the individual citizen will sue a governing body. In 1899, a citizen named Walter Smith sued the City of Brooklyn for damages caused, allegedly, by the draining of a stream and pond on his land. (This was when trees still grew in Brooklyn.) Mr. Smith, who ran an icehouse and boat-building operation, had dammed a stream running through his premises in Brooklyn, and the small pond which resulted was used in his work. Brooklyn built an aqueduct twenty-four hundred feet to the north of the pond, and with an elaborate system of conduits, wells and pumps, drained the area dry. Mr. Smith won his case in the highest court in New York, and Brooklyn was ordered to pay him for his pond.

As this is being written, a landmark case has just been adjudicated by the Fifth Circuit Court of Appeals. The Court has ruled that a declining underground water table on a Texas farm represents the depletion of a "natural deposit" as defined under the income tax code. This means that water for the first time may join that list of valuable "depletable re-sources"—oil and gas, commercial clay and ores—for which the property owner is entitled to a tax deduction by reason of the lowering value of his lands.

It started when a Texas farmer named Marvin Shurbet in 1959 deducted $377.91 from his income before figuring his tax. The revenue agents had a fit. Shurbet had labeled the item: "depletion allowance for exhaustion of underground water supply, a natural mineral deposit." The IRS stressed that "water" was not specifically listed in the code as a "deple-table resource" and claimed the taxpayer had not adequately shown that the exhaustion of his water had depreciated the value of his land. But the Court held directly against the agency on both counts and for the taxpayer. Surely water is as essential to the farmer as oil to the oil man.

And throughout the world, bleak and barren stretches of once-productive land give silent but irrefutable testimony to the truth that water is, verily, a *depletable resource*. Deserts which once were Edens lie forgotten and useless, yellowed dunes of sun-bleached nothing. No tax is paid upon their produce now, for—with the water dried away—they no longer have any productive worth.

Blackstone sets forth the following general legal guide with respect to water rights:

Water is a movable, wandering thing, and must of necessity continue common by the law of nature, so that I can have only a temporary, transient, usufructuary property therein.

As a general matter, water in its natural state ordinarily has been regarded in law as real property, and except for the "temporary, transient, usufructuary" rights held by riparian owners—those through whose land the water passes—the realty is held by the state in trust for all the citizens.

But more and more, since water is indeed a "movable, wandering thing" which travels with a cavalier disdain for state and property lines, and since demand in an ever increasing number of cases is growing to exceed supply, the federal government more and more will be called upon to perform the role of the ditchrider.

Problems cascade one upon the other, multiplying the potential for lasting good or irremedial harm. The unanswered questions mount up in a growing pile:

Just how much water must a community be assured—and in what condition?

Precisely how much pollution is too much? And who is to be held accountable?

When there is not water enough to go around, just which uses are to be given priority? Drinking water first, of course. But after that—irrigation or industry?—recreation or navigation?—stream flow or conservation storage?

When and under exactly what conditions is it proper to transfer the commodity from one watershed to another?

And if we ever really should learn to make it rain, just who is to decide where, and when?

These are but a few of the questions we'd better be prepared to answer. For they are the questions of a thirsty land.

And their answers in some cases would tax the wisdom of Solomon.

4 Dying Waters

"There are (areas) which can now keep nothing but bees but which, not so very long ago . . . produced boundless (nurture for civilization). The annual supply of rainfall was not lost, as it is at present, but was stored in potter's earth which was able to discharge the drainage of the heights into the hollows in the form of springs and rivers . . . The shrines (of decayed civilizations) that survive to the present day on the sites of extinct water supplies are evidence for the correctness of my present hypothesis."

—Plato (fifth century B.C.)

When Captain General Hernando Cortez had completed his conquest of the Aztecs of Mexico City in 1521, he had taken possession of an Indian city of great beauty and charm. Not the least of the attractions was a series of five splendid azure lakes which sparkled in the sunshine. Spanish destruction of Montezuma's capital was followed by a massive building program. Today, the old sections of the great cosmopolitan city reveal the results of the Spaniards' program of "urban renewal."

What is not visible is the group of five blue lakes. One rather dingy and receding body of water is the lone reminder of what the Aztecs found when in the early fourteenth century they came upon the site that was to become Mexico City.

Downtown Mexico City today rests on the bed of one of the lakes, long dead. The drying subsoil has caused some of the heavier structures, such as the Palace of Fine Arts, to suffer sinkage.

The city itself, in fact, for half a century has been sinking at the rate of about two inches per year as the lower ground strata, like a sponge from which the water is squeezed, compress. Modern engineering techniques, however, have solved this problem in the newer construction, as towering skyscrapers in the center of the city testify.

Yet another former lake bed, that of the once beautiful blue Lake Tuzuco, is covered today by the huge International Airport. Two other of the five lakes have simply disappeared.

What caused these lakes to die?

According to Aztec history, the wandering Aztecs, in or about the year 1325, came upon an eagle perched on a stem of prickly pear holding a serpent in his talons, his wings spread to the rising sun. Beyond him lay a broad, blue lake. They knew they had found their "promised land," the location on which to build their city. Had not a seer foreseen just such an omen?

Thus was Mexico City founded on its present site, on an island in the center of a huge body of water seventy-five hundred feet above sea level. At that time the entire area surrounding the cluster of lakes was covered with lush, green vegetation. Large cypress, oak, larch and other trees abounded. Their leafy boughs gave shade to the lakesides and their roots drew succor from the waters. Native grasses held the topsoil in place. The Aztecs left most of this natural growth, and the waters of the five lakes of the Valley of

Mexico remained in relatively the same condition throughout the two centuries of Aztec supremacy.

The *conquistadores* had different ideas. With a whim more nostalgic than sensible, they proceeded to turn the plateau into something that would remind them more of the flat, brown lands of their native Spain. They quickly denuded the soil of its verdure and began a systematic elimination of the forests. This was the first step in effecting the eventual doom of the waters of the valley.

The main source of fuel was charcoal. This caused an even more drastic recession of the forests. And as the forests receded, so did the level of the water in the lakes. Destruction of the ground cover deprived the soil of its vegetative protection, and each rain washed a bit more of the exposed land into the waters. Silt began to fill the lakes. This phenomenon was probably hastened by the high altitude, which induces a more rapid evaporation of water than at lower levels. The bare sunbaked plateau gradually lost its capacity to retain moisture, and the drying-out process now became steadily more accelerated. This process was to be a slow and almost unnoticed one, hardly perceptible save to the very old who insisted they could remember when the waters covered much more of the land. But everybody knows that old people exaggerate notoriously and hardly anyone paid much attention. The water was still sufficient for the needs of the population, so, why worry about it?

As the slow deterioration of the lakes progressed, the soil became encrusted with salt residues, remnants of the receding and evaporating water. One of the lakes was artificially dried up by man for the exploitation of salt. As the population grew, the encroachments on the forest proceeded apace. Nobody paused to ponder what kind of a heritage they were leaving their heirs. Finally the lakes were gone. Like very old men, they just shriveled up and died.

Today the Mexican government, faced with one of the most critical water problems in the Western Hemisphere, is fighting a valiant battle to resolve the shortage which plagues their principal city. Rigid laws have been enacted to salvage what remains of the water supply.

No tree may be cut down without permission. Reforestation of the entire area is being conducted at an ever-increasing rate. Water is being piped in from distant mountain streams and lakes. Pumping of underground resources is prohibited. Every possible step is being taken to correct the near-disaster which preceding generations bequeathed the 5½ million modern-day residents of Mexico City.

But, what about our own five lakes? The Great Lakes, they are called. Their story contains some disquieting parallels.

The Great Lakes form the largest single body of fresh water in the world. The word "fresh" is used in this sense merely to distinguish it from salt water. The present condition of the Great Lakes actually makes a farce of the adjective in its commonly accepted meaning.

More than 28 million human beings populate the area around the Great Lakes. One of every eight Americans resides in the Great Lakes basin. Across the border, one of every three citizens of Canada lives in the area. Many millions more in both nations are directly affected by what happens to these lakes and their waters. Health and esthetics aside, the economic consequences are beyond calculation.

All five lakes today are in dire need of immediate and concentrated attention, if future generations are to enjoy the benefits which these bodies of water have conferred upon our civilization.

Lake Erie can be accurately described as "dying." So polluted is it today that recently a Cleveland newspaper observed that if a citizen were to take a pail of water from the lake and deposit it on a municipal property he could be charged with committing a public nuisance.

In 1964, experts carried out a series of oxygen studies of the lake basin. The central core of Lake Erie was found to be for all purposes a dead body of water, so lacking in oxygen that any marine life entering the area is doomed. It is a vast underwater "desert."

Daily this "dead" area spreads. Already it measures twenty-six hundred square miles, more than one-fourth of the huge reservoir's entire surface. Merely to maintain Lake Erie's thoroughly unsatisfactory status quo will require the combined intensive efforts of all the sprawling communities adjacent to the lake as well as all of those discharging wastes into the streams which feed the lake. It also will require the voluntary cooperation and perhaps the intensive policing of the greatest and most diverse industrial complexes in the world. A concerted "crash" program designed to save the lake will take decades. The dollar estimates for the task go into the billions.

Lake Erie is not only blighted by the municipal and industrial waste from those communities which border its shrinking shorelines. It is also defiled by more than twenty grossly polluted streams. One of them, the Cuyahoga River, recently was found to contain four times the bacteria count expected in a stream of raw sewage. A daily burden of disease-ridden filth enters the estuary. Most of the streams which empty sluggishly into the lake could be aptly described as flowing cesspools.

Merely to stop the man-made pollution which daily adds to the problem would not be to solve it, however. Another part of the problem is involved in the millions of pounds of materials already in the lake which are speeding up the process of decay. These nutrients, primarily nitrogen and phosphorous, have been deposited for years by wind and rain and animal life. Algae, the green scum of microscopic living organism that feeds on these elements, draw oxygen from the air and from the water. When algae float near the surface, they sometimes restore oxygen to the lake in such volume that the fish are choked through overexposure. But as the organism sinks toward the lake's bottom, it draws more oxygen from the waters and adds to the enormous and expanding "dead sea" in the bed of the central basin.

Is Lake Erie condemned to die? Can we offer a reprieve? The time is fast approaching when it will be too late to save the lake.

Nor is Erie the only one of the Great Lakes beset with decay. It is merely the most advanced case.

By 1965, the water level in all five of the lakes had dropped to the lowest point in recorded history. Both Lake Erie and Lake Huron are fully five feet lower than they were a dozen years ago. Michigan and Ontario show similar depletion. Lake Superior is the least affected, since the locks at Sault St. Marie do control its water level to a degree.

Just how significant is all this? A one-foot drop in the water level of the Great Lakes chain results in a loss of 2.75 *trillion* (2,750,000,000,000) cubic feet of water. At our present rate of consumption, this loss is equivalent to an eighty-day supply of water for the entire nation. Thus, if all five lakes were to lose five feet before the trend is reversed, a one-year supply of our national water needs would be dissipated.

Some rather appalling results have been reported to the Congress as the water levels fall and the lake shores recede.

Ships run aground well offshore from piers which once extended far out into the water, and now stand uselessly in noisome mud. In one instance at Sandusky, Ohio, not long ago, an iron-ore vessel was grounded ten feet offshore, though the dockside level had been ample, just a few months earlier, to handle the draught of the boat.

All around the Great Lakes, marina docks sit high and dry, no longer near the water. The bathhouse at Oconto Beach, Wisconsin, has been left fully a quarter of a mile from the retreating shoreline. In the same area, waterfront cottages, which once delighted summer vacationers with the sound of waves slapping at the shore, now look more than a little silly on their stilts, a mile from the nearest water. One resident whose cottage was built on an islet which jutted a mile out into the surrounding waters now is so isolated from the lake that he has to drive to the nearest shoreline by automobile.

Elsewhere, pipes, formerly underwater, spew forth the foul discharge from septic tanks and sewage treatment plants onto the slime-covered ground and rocks, hundreds of feet from the water which should be carrying the mess away. The sight, smell and potential for disease are prodigious.

One ship construction firm in Canada is threatened with a

complete closing, since its plant is rapidly fading inland—
without, of course, moving an inch. A fish-processing firm,
built originally on the shoreline, no longer can bring its daily
catch to its docks for unloading. The docks today are sur-
rounded by dry land. Trucks must go several miles to a marina
to meet the incoming fishing vessels.

The shrinking lakes are dragging the area's economy down
with them. A chain reaction is beginning to be felt throughout the country.

The Great Lakes' shipping industry estimates the losses
brought by the lowering levels in the lakes at nearly $100
million annually. More than seven hundred ships ply these
waters, and lake shrinkage has cut total shipping by approximately 9.6 million tons annually. Every time a one-inch drop
occurs in the water level, the average tonnage which can be
carried is reduced by another fifty to a hundred tons per vessel. The series of locks throughout portions of the Great Lakes
system was designed for higher water levels. Each one-inch
drop makes the smaller locks inaccessible for the bigger ships,
and ties up traffic at larger locks while the vessels wait to file
through. Hours of waiting at roughly two hundred dollars
per hour, add further to the costs of waterborne shipping,
already penalized through reduced tonnage. Lighter loads,
more trips to deliver the goods, and waiting costs, result inevitably in higher unit prices for the eventual consumer. So
each of us, no matter where he lives in the United States,
finds his own pocketbook directly involved in the Great Lakes
problem.

More than 200 million tons of iron ore, grains, manufactured products, coal and newsprint are carried on these lakes.

101

Imagine how much iron ore goes into the steel which eventually returns to Detroit to produce automobiles. The higher cost of transporting such materials must eventually reach you and me as ultimate consumers.

Also, our foreign trade, in the most competitive period of our history, is facing trouble, since nearly 40 million tons of the total carried goes out to world markets via the St. Lawrence Seaway.

Electric power is another industry which has a great stake in the well-being of the lakes. Huge power generating companies abound all around the lakes. Many millions of people draw their electrical power from plants which depend on an adequate depth of water in the lakes.

For some time these power companies have been deeply concerned with the alarming drop in water levels. A lower volume of water reduces power output and results in higher production costs—and again, the consumer foots the bill.

One power-generating company did a detailed study of the low-water problem and decided that an answer, or at least part of it, rested with preventing the City of Chicago from withdrawing the waters of Lake Michigan in such prodigious quantities. The complainant was the Power Authority of Massena, New York, a city located on the Grass River, three miles from the St. Lawrence, and six hundred miles from Chicago. Thus does the water problem generate massive chain reactions. As a matter of fact, as the water flows, the distance between Massena and Chicago is well over a thousand miles.

Arguing their case in the federal courts, the attorneys for Massena pointed out that Chicago was diverting thirty-two hundred cubic feet of water per second from the lake to maintain navigation levels and sewage dilution; that a greater percentage of this water never returned to Lake Michigan, being lost to the Chicago shipping canal and river, eventually flowing into the Mississippi via the Illinois River. This loss of water, they contended, had caused a permanent lowering of the lakes, and was costing $2 million in electrical production capacity for every thousand cubic feet per second of water so diverted. Other interested communities joined in this suit, which asked the U.S. Supreme Court to force Chicago to reduce the intake of water to five hundred cubic feet per second, less than one-sixth its accustomed intake.

As of this writing, the case is still under consideration.

Lakes are not the only bodies of water that die. Rivers die, too. In our own time, the death rate of rivers has increased fantastically. Sometimes the killer has been erosion and siltation. Sometimes the murderer has been pollution. Often the crime has been committed by a combination of the two.

One of the most notorious victims is the fabled Hudson River, which flows for 306 miles from its source in the Adirondacks to the Atlantic.

Captain Henry Hudson discovered the river by accident in 1609 when he was searching for the Northwest Passage. He was delighted with the beauty of the land through which this mighty stream worked its way. "A pleasant land to see," he wrote in the log of his ship, the *Half Moon*.

There is nothing pleasant about the Hudson today. The river winds its way through malodorous shorelines, blighted and decayed. Its waters are fed by open sewer pipes. It has been called by *Newsweek* magazine "a fetid dumping ground" (August 23, 1965), and in 1951, the New York City Board of Water Supply formally branded it "an open running sewer."

The rape of the Hudson began in the late nineteenth century when the lumber interests stripped the hillsides of the valley and dumped the pulpy remnants of their operation into the water. They were followed by the sand and gravel operators who attacked the denuded banks and glutted the channel with countless tons of dirt. In the first years of the twentieth century, petrochemical plants, rendering plants, metal fabricators and other industries grew up on the river's shores and poured ugly streams of poisonous residue into the tormented waters.

Today upstate cities, far removed from the main body of the Hudson, add their contribution of filth. Utica, for instance, which lies more than a hundred miles from the Hudson, every day dumps 15 million gallons of raw sewage into the Mohawk River and all this finds its way to the principal stream. Albany and Rochester each dump another 60 million gallons, and New York City adds 450 million.

Thus have men destroyed the stream which provided the principal reason New York was settled in the first place.

The Hudson was once a fisherman's paradise. Today there are no more fish in parts of the river, except for a particularly repulsive type of eel which thrives on human wastes.

As it approaches New York City the river is a breeding ground for the typhoid germ. Its waters carry sickness, death, the danger of plague. Even in its current crisis of drought, New York City does not dare to tap the Hudson. With all our progress in science we apparently have not yet learned to make these foul and deadly waters useful to man.

Perhaps the Hudson can someday be brought back to life. Governor Nelson Rockefeller and others have shown a willingness to undertake a long-range planning program to revive the river. But the program will take decades and billions of dollars before it makes any headway.

Although the case of the Hudson River is the most famous example of massive, irresponsible pollution, it is by no means unique. There are hundreds of other rivers in our land that have been equally despoiled. Almost every industrial city has its particular victim. Year by year once-pure streams are being made inaccessible and useless to us.

But man is not the only murderer of rivers. Nature, also, takes a hand in the killing. Natural erosion is another part of the problem. (The most spectacular example of this, of course, is the Grand Canyon, which once, in prehistoric times, was a fertile valley supporting an early race of men as well as abundant vegetation.)

Man, the spoiler, has hastened the processes of erosion by denuding hillsides and banks so they are washed by the rains into the rivers, which eventually become choked by the sand and mud. But nature must bear a share of the blame.

An example of the power of nature is offered by a geological study of Virginia completed in 1940 by the geologist, Charles Butts. From his extensive studies he came up with an interesting theory: According to the testimony available, it would appear that during the Paleozoic era, beginning approximately 600 million years ago and ending about 230 millions years ago, more than sixty thousand cubic *miles* of sand, mud and gravel were deposited in what now constitutes the Appalachian Valley of Virginia. This deposit, in places, is eight to ten miles thick. If it were spread over the southeast end of the Blue Ridge, from which most of it probably originated, it would raise the overall altitude of the state to ten thousand feet above sea-level.

The relationship between soil erosion and sedimentation in major rivers and harbors has never been exactly determined, but we know it is significant. It is even more significant in the smaller rivers and creeks, most of which feed the larger streams. Whole valleys, since colonial settlement, have been appreciably aggraded as a result of increased erosion rates following the clearing and cultivation of tributary uplands.

One such area is the Piedmont of South Carolina, where the flood plains of the narrow, comparatively youthful valleys during the past 150 years have been aggraded by the deposition of red, micaceous sandy silt, because of erosion brought about by agricultural pursuits. These deposits average about four feet in thickness which, according to Stafford C. Happ (*American Journal of Science*, March 1945) is equivalent to the removal of about 3.1 inches from the tributary uplands.

If this sounds rather technical, the results are both apparent and tragic. The sand deposits, by filling the rivers and making them shallower, cause frequent flood damage on about 80,000 acres of corn and 40,000 acres of cleared pasture. Approximately 180,000 more acres, which should be under heavy cultivation, are now useful only for woodland pasture. Even this use is being reduced progressively by sand overwash. Every flood adds to the encroaching ruin of land that is basically fertile and should be highly productive.

This intrusion of silt in our streams is never-ending and as our water resources dwindle, it becomes a more serious problem. Even the Mississippi River is being victimized.

During hearings in late 1963 and early 1964 concerning proposed amendments to the Water Pollution Control Act, Fred Schwengel, then a Congressman from Iowa, said:

I would like to ask about another problem in connection with water pollution. That is the nondecomposable parts of pollution of rivers, the silt coming out of our most valuable resource, the land, on which we produce the food. Recently, with the help of some college boys at the University of Iowa, we did a research job on the Mississippi River, and we found that behind the Keokuk Dam in Iowa there are now 8 million carloads of silt that was not there when the dam was built. You can find up to 2 million carloads behind almost any dam on the Mississippi River, we estimate.

Similarly, another historic waterway, the Potomac, is so loaded with silt and sediment that it rides today six to seven feet above its former bed.

This is a widespread problem and it has a great effect on our water supplies. The silt builds up until it starts to choke the stream which is finally unable to digest or dissolve it. This slows down the flow-rate of the river perceptibly, in much the same way that a freight train slows down when it enters the yards. The result is a sluggish stream, less useful, less pure, less tractable. In the same way, sediment fills up our reservoirs, reducing their useful lives.

Sometimes man plays the fool, despite the very best intentions. The Florida Everglades National Park, for example, has been dealt an apparent death-stroke by the U.S. Army Corps of Engineers, which is usually on the side of the angels in these matters.

With grim single-mindedness the Engineers in 1962 constructed a "flood control basin" to contain the waters of Lake Okeechobee, which lie about fifty miles north of the Everglades and nourish the area. The purpose of the basin was not only to minimize the danger of floods, but also to conserve water for irrigation purposes.

The basin works too well. Water stopped flowing into the Everglades, and in two years this has caused irreparable damage. The Everglades is dying fast. Congress has voted the Corps $400,000 to "re-evaluate" their miscalculation, but the program will take two years, and the Everglades may not have two years to live.

This amounts to more than the murder of a national park. The Everglades supplies nutrients for the fish population of the southern section of our country, extending thousands of miles along the Gulf Stream and even reaching New England and the Maritime Provinces of Canada. The Everglades, in short, was the fountainhead of one of the largest natural food chains in the Western Hemisphere.

There are few living fish in the Everglades today. Even the mudfish are disappearing and they are usually the last to go. The picture of devastation was dramatically presented in an editorial in the Miami *Herald* (May 23, 1965):

The stench of dead fish is in the air—there is no water to be seen and bass, bream, and other fish are dead by the thousands. Hungry otters, in a desperate attempt to keep alive, make a skillful surgical incision to extract the liver of dead garfish. Raccoons have set up garbage hunting parties. The only fish left are the mudfish—and they're making a "last ditch effort." A common sight is a larger alligator eating its smaller more helpless brother in a nauseating act of cannibalism. This spring, no longer were there multitudes of nesting waterfowl—there is no longer any food. The only really active wildlife here are the vultures constantly circling overhead.

Water catastrophes are not only caused by greedy and careless human beings, they are sometimes caused by well-meaning conservationists, too. The effect, however, is the same: less usable water, less fishlife, a decay of natural beauty, and a serious blow to the economy.

5 "... Nor Any Drop to Drink"

"Water, water, everywhere . . ."
        —Coleridge: *"The Rime of the Ancient Mariner"*

"Flush twice; Dallas needs the water."
        —Author Unknown (*Graffito discovered on wall
        of a Fort Worth rest room*)

Water pollution has been with us ever since the beginning of civilization, but each advance in our growing society has made it worse. In an earlier day, man seldom did anything about it because he simply did not realize that foul streams were imperiling his health and possibly even the future of the race. When he first began realizing it, he didn't have the tools to cope with it.

In fact, one drink of water from the polluted Potomac River could well have changed the entire course of American history. The drinker was the youthful George Washington. One day while fishing he slaked his thirst from the muddy river. The water at that point was so contaminated that he contracted a bad case of the "flux," or dysentery, and narrowly escaped death. It took the best doctors in Virginia to pull him through. Whether he survived because of, or in spite of, their ministrations is problematical.

Another famous victim of polluted water was Junius Brutus Booth, the American actor and father of Edwin and John Wilkes Booth. He drank of the contaminated Mississippi and was dead of typhoid within two days.

Our ignorance of waterborne diseases had a significant effect on our infant mortality rate during the eighteenth and early nineteenth centuries. If an infant was sturdy enough to live through the highly hazardous moments of childbirth, it usually survived the first year. However, the mortality rate in the second year was very high indeed. This was because during the first year an infant lived on either its mother's milk, or on boiled cow's milk. But, during the second year, the infant was given water, and this brought on "summer complaints," or *cholera infantum,* a disease we now know as typhoid fever. It was usually fatal. The solution to this deadly problem seems so simple today.

But it is not quite so simple as we think it is.

While it is true that we know the evils of pollution and have known them for at least a century, we still continue to befoul our waters with a reckless abandon.

Today almost all our major sources of natural water are to some degree polluted. We have seen what has happened to Lake Erie and the other Great Lakes. There is not an important river basin in the United States which is uncontaminated.

The situation is so bad that its cure is going to require a massive national effort, calling into action not only the federal government but also state and local authorities, as well as the cooperation of every individual citizen. The alternative is the creation of a huge liquid desert: ample water, but unfit for use. If we delay too long the trend will be irreversible. The continent could become a wasteland.

And I am not talking about a thousand years from now, or even a hundred, necessarily. I am talking about something that could happen to us within the next few generations; in the first quarter, let us say, of the twenty-first century.

We might ask why our forefathers, who were so bright about so many other things, were so shortsighted about our water supply? The answer can only be found in our own imperfect natures. Man always wastes those things he possesses in abundance. We ravaged our forests; we used up millions upon millions of acres of our valuable topsoil; we destroyed and vulgarized much of our incomparable scenery. At present we are not only destroying our water sources, but we are also destroying the air we breathe.

Characteristically we finally take corrective measures when it is almost too late. Maybe the horse isn't entirely gone when we lock the barn gate, but it is usually at least halfway out. The process of getting the horse back into the stable is usually painful and arduous.

With water pollution, we were in the position of a man with a killing disease who does not become aware of it until it has progressed almost too far.

Before the turn of the century we were primarily an agrarian nation. Most of our river basins were sprinkled with communities of reasonable size, sufficiently separated from each other to permit nature's filtering process to dissolve, dissipate and absorb the waste from one community before it reached the water intakes of the next town downstream.

During the early twentieth century, "progress" wrought many changes. Our industrial base began to expand; our rural way of life began to contract. People settled much closer together, building factories and concentrating in communities which were themselves growing closer together. Greater concentrations of sewage and industrial wastes were dumped into the rivers, with less time and distance for the cleaning process to take place.

It used to be a rule of thumb that a river would cleanse itself in seven miles. While this was never really accurate, it became wildly erroneous when we complicated the cleansing job of the stream by dumping more and more industrial wastes of an increasingly toxic nature into the water.

Our forefathers eventually recognized the problem sufficiently to start treating the water before distributing it to the users in their communities. But that was as far as they went. Once the water was used, it was dumped untreated back into the river. The streams became more and more contaminated as they rolled on their way to the sea.

The scope of the problem can be judged by the following figures:

In 1900, the United States had a population of 76 million. Less than one-third of the population had access to a sewer system. And fewer than a million were connected to sewer systems that treated sewage before discharging it back into the streams.

In 1920, we had a population of 106 million. About 48 million of these (or around 36 per cent) used sewers. Less than 10 million were connected to treated sewers.

By 1950, we had more than 150 million people. Fifty-three

113

per cent of these (or about 80 million) were connected to sewers, and 61 million of them were using treated sewers.

Currently we have an estimated 190 million people. Sixty-three per cent (or 120 million) use sewer systems, and of this number 100 million are connected to treated systems.

This looks like real progress. But since 1900, the amount of untreated *industrial* waste introduced into our rivers has increased by so much that there is no sense in even attempting a comparison. Furthermore, man has, as we have seen, devised ways of using grossly larger amounts of the water supply than his predecessors had used. It is estimated that we are now dumping sewage into our streams equivalent to that of 117 million people in 1900. Of this amount, the raw sewage is equivalent to what 30 million people produced in 1900.

And, of course, all this is being discharged into rivers that are already sick and dying from gross misuse over the years.

In our struggle to control pollution we seem to take four steps backward for every three we take forward.

When discussing the pollution problem we must not forget those millions who do not have access to sewers. As we all know, these people are not all rural residents in backward areas dependent upon the primitive outhouse and the community pump. A large percentage are suburban dwellers relying upon septic fields to take away their sewage. As these suburban communities grow, the underground waters become incapable of absorbing the excessive discharge and they can no longer purify themselves. It is a common occurrence to hear that health authorities in certain areas have refused to issue any more septic tank permits, or have even closed down housing developments under construction because the underground waters have become just as polluted as the surface streams.

Such a case occurred a few years ago in Potomac, Maryland, one of the really "in" suburbs of Washington, D.C. Potomac is in the heart of the horse and fox-hunting country, and its estates include some of the most fabulous in the country. In this area a septic tank was kind of a status symbol, indicating that you had the leisure and the means to live deep enough in the country so you wouldn't have to share a sewer system with the *hoi polloi*. Without warning, however, one subdivision of new homes in Potomac, ranging in price from $65,000 to $125,000 found its water supply foul, unusable and dangerous. The health authorities forbade the use of the underground supplies, and a substantial number of people who had moved proudly into $100,000 suburban estates found they could not live in them because they had no water. At great expense, the subdivision had to be hooked onto the nearest sewer lines. The new suburbanites lost their status symbols, but they retained their health.

Underground waters are also menaced, of course, by salt —another major cause of pollution. When areas located near the sea depend upon underground sources (like Brevard County, Florida, mentioned earlier), salt water intrudes whenever overuse causes the underground table to drop below a certain level. This makes the supply next to useless. Population concentration is causing this condition in far too many localities along the Atlantic Coast.

Strangely enough, bodies of fresh water, even without man's interference, must fight to stay alive. It is evidently the

115

inexorable will of nature to replace water with land, and most of our lakes would *eventually* disappear even if man did not inhabit the earth. But the process of disappearance would consume millennia. It is the intrusion of man that has reduced the time gap to a few generations.

Fresh water is never really pure. Every rainfall collects some mild contamination as it passes through the atmosphere. Even rivers protected by a heavy umbrella of undergrowth and vegetation receive some silt from the rain.

This is natural pollution. It is increased when the fish and other waterlife die, and by the death of vegetation. But under natural conditions, a semblance of biological status quo is maintained by actions which take place in fresh waters.

Water is the greatest solvent in the world, and it breaks down foreign matter. Also, fresh water contains large amounts of oxygen, gathered from the atmosphere and from green plantlife.

Besides, there is a form of bacteria in fresh water called *aerobium* which needs oxygen to survive and can act as a hero or a villain in the life or death of a body of water, depending on certain outside influences.

The aerobic agents act somewhat like the corpuscles in our bloodstream. They fight infection where they find it, and they do an excellent job as long as they are kept in balance and under control.

When a foreign element is introduced into a stream, such as dead marine or plant life, the aerobia attack it, live off it and consume it. As they eat, they multiply rapidly. They are wonderful scavengers in a reasonably clean body of water. They turn the solids back into clean water and when the foreign elements are consumed, they die off and disappear.

However, when the population along the river banks increases, and factories grow up to supply its needs, the stream becomes more seriously polluted. Its oxygen is diminished. The aerobia consume all they can get, denying it more and more to other marine life and plant life. Thus, the aerobia which started out as friends, become enemies of the stream. As pollution increases, the weaker kinds of fish and plants begin to die off, adding to the contamination.

Meanwhile, lurking in the depths of the stream, unknown and unseen, are the beginnings of another form of death. These are the *anaerobic* bacteria, a germ that hates oxygen and sunlight.

As the overload of waste builds up and the proliferating factories pour their mass of chemical filth into the water, including death-dealing sulphur, the aerobia consume all the oxygen that is left. All other life dies off, in much the same way as a human being in an advance stage of emphysema. When the oxygen is gone, the aerobia die, too.

This is when the anaerobic colony takes over the river. As the sludge and filth and human waste build up, the anaerobia can operate at will, since the water is too dirty to permit much penetration by the sun, and the oxygen is all but gone. They pull out the hydrogen elements in the water and absorb the sulphur elements in industrial waste. This causes the river, which already has become unsightly, to give off the characteristically evil stench of dead water.

The river has now become little more than an open sewer. Many of the factories that caused the condition in the first place will now find the water too foul to use. They pack up

117

and move elsewhere to another stream which they will soon contaminate in the same way as they did the first.

They leave behind a desolated city. Jobs become scarce because of the departing industry. Merchants suffer from dwindling business. The piers of bridges, wharves and the boats begin to corrode. The treating plants cannot handle the bacteria in the water or dispel its nauseating taste. New water sources for the city must be found, usually many miles away. This costs money, which the hard-hit municipality can ill afford. The community's economy begins to wither and rot. It becomes an almost universal slum.

Meanwhile the useless river flows sluggishly by its front door.

This sordid drama is being repeated constantly throughout the country. There is a limit to the number of times it can be repeated. We are running out of rivers.

How dangerous is a contaminated river?

The Connecticut River, beautiful as it works its rustic way dividing upper Vermont and New Hampshire, is perverted into a stinking filth conduit after it passes through Lebanon, New Hampshire, and heads through Springfield, Holyoke, Chicopee and Hartford. One sampling of its waters revealed the bacteria of typhoid, paratyphoid, cholera, salmonellosis, tuberculosis, anthrax, tetanus and all the known viruses, including polio, and tape-, round-, hook- and pin-worms as well as blood flukes.

One of the standards for clean water is the coliform count. The coliform is a rod-shape bacterium found typically in human waste. The minimum coliform count usually tolerated for swimming is 1,000 per 100 millimeters of water (about half a cup). The count on the Connecticut reached a peak of 947,000 per 100 millimeters at Chicopee.

The Detergent Invasion

But silt and sludge and industrial and human wastes are not the only mortal foes a river has. One of the most formidable of all enemies is, ironically, an enemy intended to produce cleanliness: the detergent.

The drama of the detergent and the nation's rivers may finally have a happy ending, or at least a satisfactory one. Time alone will tell.

Several years ago, I came across an interesting photograph in a newspaper, showing some men shoveling what appeared to be snow. The caption pointed out that the white substance was really soapsuds created by the discharge into the Mississippi River near Dubuque, Iowa, of detergents from the kitchens of the city. The men had been fishing on a dock. Behind them a huge and surprising mound of suds had been created, blocking their path back to the shore. So heavy was the mess that shovels were brought into play from nearby boats so they could dig their way out. This picture was so dramatic that it was later introduced in congressional hearings on the subject of synthetic detergents and their role in pollution.

Prior to seeing this picture, I had heard and read of similar incidents; incidents which seemed to increase almost daily. But it was this one picture which triggered a memory, going back to the spring of 1947. I was eating lunch at the counter in a drug store. Nearby were two women, obviously shoppers, who also had dropped in for a snack. They were not so busily engaged in conversation that they didn't pay attention to one of the waitresses washing a stack of dirty dishes. She would take a stack of plates or saucers, put them in a sink filled with what appeared to be clear, or reasonably clear, water, rinse them and then put them in a second sink of what also appeared to be water. One of the ladies observed the performance and asked, "Waitress, aren't you going to wash those dishes in anything else?" "No," replied the young girl, "Won't be necessary. This stuff is a new kind of soap that doesn't make suds."

That caused a few comments, most of which centered around the contention that anything that washed without suds was far from sanitary. What irritates me now is the recollection that I found myself silently agreeing with the housewives. I now have learned that suds have no value at all; they are not a cleansing agent, merely the aftereffect of sundry soap formulae.

In fact, as recently as the early twentieth century, few soaps made an appreciable amount of suds at all. But gradually we became conditioned to suds through the advertising campaigns of the soap companies who centered their competition in the market place on the amount of "rich, billowy" suds their product could whip up in a sink. Our minds subconsciously associated sudsiness with cleanliness.

An advance in soap processes, it was thought, was the introduction of synthetic detergents to the American market. After World War II the synthetic detergent was invented in Germany because of the extreme shortage of fats from which to make soap. Detergents were developed to the point where they were superior for most uses to the original product. They were better than soap, but they went over on the American market like a lead balloon because they didn't make suds. That problem was easily solved by putting in sudsing agents, and away we went again on an orgy of more and more suds per product.

Not too long after the introduction of suds-producing synthetic detergents into the commercial market, their sales passed those of ordinary soap products, by far. Today more than 90 per cent of the cleansing agents sold in this country are detergents.

However, soon after the popularity of detergents was established, large amounts of suds began to appear on rivers around the country. That marked the beginning of a lengthy tug-of-war among the manufacturers, the health authorities and finally the Congress of the United States.

Among hundreds of reports of mountains of suds on our waterways was one from the Wisconsin State Board of Health, which said a "wall of foam thirty-five feet wide, three hundred feet long, and fifteen feet high" had been observed in the Mississippi River. In Montgomery County, Maryland, residents found steady streams of foam coming out of their taps, the results of excessive amounts of detergent wastes getting into their water supply. Another official report described a forty-foot wall of suds in the Rock River, in Illinois. There were many others.

One witness before the House Public Works Committee reported that sudsing of streams had even created a hazard to auto traffic: Suds from rivers alongside highways had blown off and covered windshields, cutting visibility to zero and causing motorists to slam on their brakes.

This was not a uniquely American problem. Even from England came the report that the swans on the Avon, at Stratford, of all places, were unable to navigate through the suds covering that historic river.

Naturally the manufacturers countered such reports with statements that occurrences of this type had no real significance, since the suds were harmless. Furthermore, they pointed out these were not exactly the suds which went down the drain, since those had long been dissipated, but were more like froth or foam created by the roiling waters.

Health authorities took a different position, stating that there was some evidence that such concentrations of undissolved detergents certainly had a bad effect on fish and, therefore, that this indicated great quantities of these materials could have a bad effect on human beings. Then suburbia, with its fields of septic tanks, often found that the undissolved wastes from the synthetic detergents had overflowed and found their way into ground water supplies.

Industry lamely said that in time someone would come up with a synthetic detergent which would break down and dissolve in water.

By 1963, things were getting more "soapy" with Cleveland, Milwaukee and other cities finding their sewage systems almost clogged by the increasing amounts of suds, causing the expenditure of hundreds of thousands of dollars in efforts to solve the problem. Still, nothing had been announced by the manufacturers which indicated a solution was forthcoming.

Since the Congress of the United States must represent the

interests of all the people, not just a small segment, it seemed to many members that the time had come for legislative action to do something about the damage produced by detergents. Among them was Congressman Henry S. Reuss of Milwaukee, Wisconsin.

Prior to his proposing an amendment to the Water Pollution Control Act, Reuss did his homework well. He traveled to Germany where, by virtue of its longer history of using these detergents, the problem was more extreme. Reuss returned with documented and shocking case histories, plus the knowledge that Germany had passed stringent legislation prohibiting the use or manufacture of undissolvable detergents after October 1964. The companies concerned either had to find a solution or stop production.

Appearing before the House Public Works Committee in December 1963 in support of his proposed amendment, the Wisconsin representative related numerous incidents of such huge amounts of suds on German rivers as almost to halt water traffic and seriously interfere with highway traffic along their banks. One report from the German Ministry of Health said that permits had been denied boaters for sluicing because their very lives were being endangered by the clogging mass of foam and suds along most of the inland waterways. So bad was the condition at times that navigation aids were enveloped in suds and the volume of suds so heavy as to make rescue operations impossible should anyone get into trouble.

Congressman Reuss went on, as follows:

Is there any harm in the presence of ABS-based detergents in our water? The answer unfortunately is yes, plenty. [ABS stands

123

for alkyl benzene sulfonate, the main cleaning ingredient in detergents and the villain of this story.]

First, they cause foam on drinking water.

Secondly, detergent pollution interferes with treatment of sewage, and adds considerably to the costs of sewage systems.

Thirdly, detergent pollution represents an unnecessary hazard to human health.

Although he agreed that there had been no substantiated cases of human beings having been adversely affected by detergent wastes, he felt that the toxic effect on fish indicated that real human health problems soon would develop.

The Congressman cited additional problems in detergent pollution, which conjured up a grim picture of a moving mountain of suds silently flowing down every stream in America. He made a most convincing case for compelling legislation, provided that the manufacturers did not come up with a satisfactory solution.

The witnesses for the detergent industry were also persuasive. They proved they were aware of the problem, although they claimed their suds were a nuisance, not a menace. They said they had high hopes for a new product which would make the problem obsolete.

Anthony Celebrezze, who was then Secretary of Health, Education, and Welfare, came before the Committee and urged that the manufacturers be given a chance to prove their good faith. The Committee, confident that a base had been established from which compelling legislation could be passed, if deemed necessary, agreed to go along with Mr. Celebrezze's recommendation.

Our faith has been, to a considerable degree, justified.

Shortly after the hearings concluded, the manufacturers announced that a major breakthrough had been achieved and that, no later than December, 1965, we would see an end of nondecomposable detergents. Actually, they beat their own deadline by six months and announced in July 1965 that all goals had been achieved.

It may well be that those frightening mountains of blowing bubbles will now disappear from our rivers, and we can all enjoy water that, even though it be far from pure, will be, at least, sudless.

Madison Avenue might well consider undertaking a public education program to undo the harm it has done in the past by selling the American housewife on the superiority of sudless detergents. If the manufacturers have come up with a product that will do the cleansing job competently without befouling our waterways, they deserve all the help they can get in selling that product.

Death Throes of an Industry

We have seen, in general, how pollution has caused severe economic losses throughout the nation. Here is a specific case history—the story of what has happened to the once-flourishing shellfish industry in the United States.

If you enjoy biting into a crisp gulf shrimp, or tasting oysters on the half-shell, or slicing into a Maryland crabcake, or savoring the flavor of a New England clam, then you had better start indulging your fancy as much as you can. It could be that these delights will soon be denied you.

Shellfish have always had a struggle to survive on the bottoms of waters. Predators devour them; movements of sea waters and hurricanes upset the delicate balance of life within their beds. In the past, they have been dredged by the millions of pounds, with no replenishment. Fish diseases affect them.

Still, through it all, they have survived.

The final threat to their useful existence could be water pollution.

Unlike other underwater creatures, which can leave contaminated areas, most shellfish young are immobile and must passively endure the ravages of disease-laden waters, which either kill them or make them unfit for human consumption.

Three hundred years ago, from Maine down the eastern seaboard, around the peninsula of Florida, into the Gulf of Mexico to the borders of Mexico, the entire shoreline was one huge bed of spawning clams, oysters, crabs, scallops, mussels and shrimp. Per capita consumption of these marine delights was astronomical. The shellfish trade created some of our greatest fortunes. We exported our product to Europe. Everyone could enjoy the various species, since the supply was great and, consequently, the price low. For three cents, for instance, one could have a whole quart of Chesapeake Bay oysters.

As with every other resource, we managed within 150 years practically to desolate the shellfish beds along the northeastern tier of states, where there was the greatest population concentration. Oysters, in particular, became scarce and, therefore, items of luxury.

However, Yankee ingenuity was not to be denied. Shortly after the turn of the nineteenth century, the beds of New

York and New Jersey were replenished with young oysters from the plentiful stocks of the Chesapeake Bay. Bit by bit, little by little, these areas were once again producing great quantities of oysters. People could once more afford to feast on them.

Matters moved along pretty well for the better part of a century, with adequate supplies of all species being available to all.

Then an alarming condition began to spread. More and more people were falling ill of typhoid, dysentery and infectious hepatitis, all waterborne diseases. In most cases, the health authorities were able to isolate the cause as being one variety of shellfish or another. The authorities soon began closing acre after acre of clam, oyster and other fish beds. As our population continued to grow, so did the blight of our polluted waters, and correspondingly still greater areas became contaminated.

Two major typhoid epidemics, in 1916 and 1924, were attributed to contaminated clams and oysters. Quite naturally this caused a general distrust of all shellfish. The industry was hard hit during each period and suffered tremendous dollar losses.

After the 1924 epidemic, in which 1,500 people were infected, and 150 died, the shellfish companies formed a compact with the United States Public Health Service, whereby interstate health controls and standards were established. Acting together as partners, the commercial and governmental agencies have accomplished wonders in maintaining sanitary safeguards in the industry.

But there are always some unscrupulous operators who cut

corners and defy the laws. There have been numerous outbreaks of waterborne diseases since 1924, but without exception, these have been minor and have been traced to poachers exploiting condemned areas and to innocents who did not comprehend the dangers of fishing in troubled waters.

As recently as 1961, there was an alarming increase in cases of infectious hepatitis in New Jersey. At least three hundred persons were stricken, with some estimates listing the total as six hundred. New Jersey health authorities, noting that most of the cases centered around Raritan Bay, soon uncovered the cause. Poachers had worked contaminated clam beds that had been closed and had sold their wares as legitimate produce, thus creating misery and near-death for hundreds of unsuspecting persons.

Let me reiterate that these recent events were caused by illegal operations conducted by persons outside the industry itself. The public normally can be assured that fish purchased from reliable sources have been gathered under strict controls exercised by the producers, as well as by local and federal agencies, and are free of contamination. The industry today is in such economic straits that I do not want to imply anything which would leave an impression that responsible companies are partners in such illegal and deadly activities.

At the turn of the twentieth century, operators were delivering millions of bushels of good produce annually from beds which were replenished, and the prospects for the future seemed most favorable. Seafood was a most popular—and healthy—source of sustenance among Americans. In 1908, when the first survey of annual production was compiled, the industry revealed a $150-million-dollar enterprise in oysters alone. Our population at that time was just over 80 million.

The Chesapeake Bay was producing between 10 to 12 million bushels of oysters annually. By 1940, production in this area was down to 4½ million, and today just about a million bushels is all that can be harvested from the huge bay in one year.

The major portion of this decline is attributed purely and simply to pollution. No legal oyster operations have been conducted in the filthy Raritan Bay for nearly forty years. Alabama officials report that pollution from steel mills, chemical and fiber plants, untreated suburban sewage and mining run-off has since 1954 caused periodic closing of its shellfish beds. More than $22 million is wasted every year because of unworkable beds. The value of the nation's oyster crop today is $55 million a year, or about one-third of what it was in 1908. In actual value, of course, the percentage is far lower because of the declining purchasing power of the dollar.

Startling reports on this subject have been presented to Congress in hearings concerning the future of the industry. A leading producer of shellfish on Long Island told a vivid tale of how pollution hit his business. In 1937, in the Great South Bay, his company produced in excess of 350,000 bushels of oysters. Their output by 1960 was zero. During the mid-1950's, for two years in a row, the quality of hardshell clam meat was so poor as to make the clams unmarketable. This was all directly due to pollution.

Gravest statistic of all, though, concerned Maryland. Less than a century ago this state produced more oysters than the rest of the world combined. Today, it has fallen behind Louisiana—currently our number one producer—and Louisiana cannot claim to be anywhere near the output level of the rest of the world.

At one time New England was the largest producer of clams in the world. Today she must import most of her supply. Pollution, again, was the most significant factor in the destruction of tremendous areas along the coast. Witness after witness has related his woes to Congress, each underscoring the rapid decline and predicting the eventual death of the industry unless something is done about pollution.

J. Richards Nelson, Chairman of the Connecticut Shellfish Commission, in citing a long list of ailments and problems facing the business in his state, reported that in the past twenty years untreated sewage, industrial pollutants and sludge have forced the removal of seedbeds to seven miles farther downstream from New Haven.

Condemned beds in Massachusetts total more than fifteen thousand acres; in Maine, in excess of seventy-five thousand acres; and in Chesapeake Bay, twenty thousand. (The latter continues to lose about five hundred acres a year.) And so the toll adds up, without the slightest relief in sight.

The trouble is not confined to the East. Puget Sound in the state of Washington has been very severely hit in recent years. Seafood producers have been locked in a major conflict with pulp and paper mills, contending their discharge of wastes, primarily an ingredient called sulfite waste liquor, is destroying the fishing industry in that part of the country. Presenting their evidence in the form of colored slides, the producers created considerable astonishment among members of the House Subcommittee on Fisheries and Wildlife Conservation. Scum and filth were visible in gross amounts. Sometimes the stains measured five miles long.

All this revolting mess adds to the pollution problem in the

Sound at a daily rate of 210 million gallons. This volume comes from just seven mills. The discharge, like any other foreign matter placed in water, creates what is termed "biological oxygen demand," or BOD. As the water attempts to break down these masses of contamination, it loses valuable oxygen. Without oxygen, fish cannot survive. This daily discharge from seven mills is equal to the human waste of a population of 8,400,000, and the latest census shows the population of the entire state of Washington as just 2,800,000.

Some pulp and paper producers have taken steps to render their output harmless, or to cut down on the totals, but others have continued to fight the issue, refusing to invest their capital in processes which would decrease the contaminating effects of their runoffs. Some producers have even threatened to close down certain facilities if the state requires them to install systems to recover most of this waste material. (Such systems exist and can recover 85 per cent of this waste.) Since each ton puts out 2,400 pounds of sulfite waste, and production is in excess of 3 million tons annually, and continues to increase with each passing year, the problem will become even more acute.

Shellfish beds throughout the area have been closed down as being polluted beyond hope of recovery. Still the mills fight against being forced to clean up their own mess, using a documented publicity program which strongly repeats the propaganda that the only solution for the problem would be closing the mills. This economic threat does have an effect on the majority of people in the area since job losses and payroll dollars would disappear if the mills shut down.

As the years have gone by, and the producers of fish have

131

fought back against every condition with which they were faced, they felt they had experienced just about everything that could possibly drive them to the wall. But still another disaster was to strike their staggering industry.

Testifying before a Congressional committee in October 1963, Mr. William P. Ballard, head of a fish and oyster company in Virginia, told the story of how his company was struggling to defeat a new and sudden killer. His story, in part, follows:

It was in the early spring of 1959 that the oyster farmer, during the normal process of gathering his oysters, noticed an abnormal mortality in the oysters. We had heard of a blight known as M.S.X. which occurred in Long Island Sound. Approximately 90 percent of the oysters planted died within a short time. We had hoped that this would not occur in the Chesapeake but our hopes were in vain. The oysters continued to die in that spring of 1959 and again in the fall. It was in the spring of 1960 that M.S.X. reached an epidemic stage, and we discontinued planting seed. Frantically, we harvested all the oysters we could, operating late in the summer—the oyster season usually runs from September through April and sometimes May. We even gathered oysters that were very small and immature in a desperate effort to stave off a financial disaster. It became a salvage operation; we were trying to save what we could.

Needless to say, we discontinued buying seed when we realized that a great catastrophe was upon us. All the planters in the lower Chesapeake discontinued their planting in March, 1960.

Mr. Ballard produced the seed oyster purchases records for his firm which showed that in 1957 more than 500,000 bushels were purchased for planting, more than 575,000 in 1958, 640,000 in 1959, but only 190,000 in 1960, a trifling

11,000 bushels in 1961 and 14,000 in 1962. This was a graphic display of the economic consequences of but one problem. Employment by his company plunged from 338 people to 21 by November 1961.

In reviewing the present and the future of the entire industry, Dr. J. L. McHugh, Bureau of Commercial Fisheries, had many things to say concerning the economic welfare of the business. Here are some of his thoughts:

The commercial fisheries of the United States, considered as a single industry, are important. The landed value of the domestic catch exceeds $350 million a year, and the retail value is 2½ to 3 times as great. It may be said, therefore, that this is a billion dollar industry. . . . The fishing industry of the United States, however, consists of many small more or less independent segments, few of which are of dominant importance locally. Therefore, when urban or industrial development impinges upon fishery interests, the fisheries often suffer. Urban development goes on relentlessly. When the economic values of manufacturing industry, residential development and fisheries come into conflict, the fisheries often come off second best.

The real threat to our commercial fishery resources comes from the insidious growth of human activity. An industrial plant here, a residential development there, an isolated spraying for mosquito control, individually do little violence to our fishery resources. But each takes its small toll, and exacts a net loss. . . . The day may not be far away when oysters and clams have gone the same way as the passenger pigeon or the buffalo in the United States.

One final statistic: The current per capita consumption of shell fish in the United States is but one-twentieth what it was ninety years ago.

And one final question: Since the common degree of pollu-

133

tion has become so lethal to the fish population, can it fail to exert a truly harmful effect upon human health?

A Universal Problem

We have focused our attention on a few rivers and other bodies of water in this discussion of pollution. I would not for the world have anyone think that the few examples I have cited are special or unique. They are merely symptomatic.

At the risk of turning some stomachs I shall engage in a short roll call of horror cases, just to give an idea of the universality of the problem which we face. Multiply these stories by a thousand and you have an approximation of the size of the crisis we face.

The Mississippi, the legendary Father of Waters, today is nothing more, in most of its majestic reaches, than just a dirty old man. It is too thick to navigate and too thin to cultivate. Everything imaginable (and many things not imaginable) is dumped into the river. Around St. Louis, for example, a chicken-treating plant located on Gravois Creek, which empties into the river, unloads the effluvia of its kill into the waters every morning.

As a member of the Congressional Committee investigating the water pollution problem I was privileged (if that is the word, which I doubt) to view some color films which Peter F. Mattei, Executive Director, Metropolitan St. Louis Sewer District, had taken of this operation. As I watched this horror I thought of Revelations XVI:1–4, the passage describing how the third angel, obeying the voice out of the temple "poured out his vial upon the rivers and the fountains of waters; and they became blood."

Up to that time I had thought St. John the Divine had, perhaps, been engaging in hyperbole in order to impress the faithful. When I saw the color films, I felt St. John was guilty of understatement. The Mississippi literally ran red with blood, and the chicken entrails and packing-house wastes were so thick upon the waters that the paddle wheels of the steamboats were fouled with them.

Chicken blood and guts cannot be destroyed normally by the flow of a clean river. Since the Mississippi is already filthy when this nauseating mess hits it, the chances of absorption are nil. The sight of the Mississippi as it flows past St. Louis is enough to make the heartiest trencherman forsake his dinner.

The list is almost endless.

The once-lovely Presumpscot, in Maine, offends the nostrils with the pungent aroma of rotten eggs, the telltale sign of hydrogen sulfide gas.

The Merrimac, once the symbol of New England's rural beauty, runs reddish brown and actually bubbles with the gases it carries.

The Mahonong in Pennsylvania is another open, running sore, suppurating industrial discharge with large blobs of scum forming a floating scab on its surface.

The Pearl (how hopeful and poetic were those who named it first!) is so vile from the discharge of paper mills and human beings that for twenty miles around Jackson, Mississippi, ranchers will not permit their cattle to water along its banks. Its bacterial density is 168 times the acceptable maximum. In southeast Georgia, the river is so foul that there is not enough oxygen to kill or assimilate any wastes whatsoever.

In the Southwest many streams *seem* clear and sparkling. In most of these streams, this is an illusion. The black precipitate of oil-grime has settled on the bottom. The water looks clean, but contains no oxygen and can support no life whatsoever.

Surely the Snake River, which runs so wild through Yellowstone Park, is almost the prototype of all clean mountain streams. But the Snake receives the filth of 50 cities and 150 industries before it vomits into the Columbia River. The Yakima and the Willamette also contribute their special eructations to the Columbia so that the nets of the fishermen sometimes become so coated with slop that they can hardly be pulled from the water.

The Missouri has been known as the Big Muddy for many years. However, nowadays, a canoe can hardly cut its way through some of its stretches as it seeps through the state which bears its name. The slaughter houses in Omaha, St. Joseph and both Kansas Cities extrude viscera and fats in such quantities that they create huge greaseballs, matrixed with animal hair, which are often mistaken for capsized canoes. But, to someone who doesn't know what is causing the phenomenon and who is mercifully devoid of the sense of tic, barbaric sight. It runs bright red, you see—with blood. It is no longer the Big Muddy; it is the Big Bloody.

The roll call of degenerate rivers need not be extended here. Every area where people and industries abound has its full share of pollution running wild, endangering health, destroying beauty, seriously denying badly needed water to the people. Every section of our land is plagued by sickening and moribund waters.

smell, the Missouri in these stretches might present a fantas-

We have in this country an affluent society.

If we don't change our ways, and soon, we shall have only an effluent society.

The sickness of our streams is caused by man. It can be cured by man, but only if action is taken with sufficient boldness and with sufficient speed.

In the next chapter, we shall see some examples of what kind of action has been taken in some areas and, far more important, what action can and must be taken in the future. It had better be the *near* future.

6 To Clean Up the Streams

"And if from man's vile arts I flee
  And drink pure water from the pump;
  I gulp down infusoria,
  And quarts of raw bacteria,
  And hideous rotatorae,
  And wriggling polygastricae,
  And slimy diatomacae,
  And various animalculae
  Of middle, high and low degree."
      —William Juniper: *"The True Drunkard's
                              Delight"*

At least 20 billion gallons of water a day are being wasted in this country by pollution. This is water that could be used and reused, if treated properly. It is ravaged water which is a menace to the health of everyone who has contact with it. It offends the nose and the eyes of all who come near it, and flows uselessly past water-hungry communities on its way to an indifferent sea.

This wasted water amounts to about 6 per cent of the total needs of the nation. It is a very significant 6 per cent, however, since it constitutes better than one-fourth of the country's *pure* water needs, and its loss adversely affects the lives, the economy, the health and the pleasure of far more than half of our population.

It should be remembered that this figure involves only surface pollution. Underground pollution is depleting our water supply with equally devastating effect.

In coastal areas, for instance, falling fresh water tables underground have permitted the intrusion of salt water into the *aquifers*, or individual water-bearing beds between subterranean rock formations. This problem has become acute in California, Maryland, New Jersey, Texas and on Long Island, New York.

In the Southwest and Midwest, disposal practices in oil fields are also causing salt pollution. Brine left in evaporation pits at oil-well sites is seeping down into the water tables. Near Tucson, Arizona—to give one example of the extreme seriousness of this problem—the underground water resources are being depleted at the rate of 3.5 million acre-feet a year. *This adds up to an annual depletion of 1.2 trillion gallons.*

Improper sewage and industrial waste disposal in permeable lands also adds to this problem of underground spoliation and depletion.

Pollution is caused by man's carelessness, indifference and callousness. It is ironic that law enforcement authorities impose sizable fines on anyone who litters up a roadside, a picnic area or a beach, but very rarely bother anyone who litters up a stream.

Pollution consists of anything that degrades the quality of the water. There are at least eight different kinds of pollution that make water use and reuse impossible and turn rivers into putrid nuisances. When these forms of pollution combine and act together in concert, they often create a chemical mess which science cannot unravel and which therefore defies our purifying plants.

The eight forms of pollution are, roughly: ordinary sewage and related organic substances; disease-carrying infectious agents; chemical plant nutrients; synthetic-organic chemicals; sediment; radioactive substances; inorganic chemicals and mineral substances; and heat.

Pollution from ordinary sewage and related organic substances is perhaps the worst; it is certainly the most embarrassing. There are 59 million Americans living in approximately two thousand cities who use sewer systems which are either partly or totally inadequate in their treatment of human wastes before those wastes are dumped into rivers and streams. Among these are some of our very largest cities. We have never attacked this, one of the most primitive problems of civilization, with sufficient boldness and forethought. With all our vaunted technology, we treat our sewage, on the whole, far less scientifically than do the reputedly backward coolies in the rice paddies of the Orient. After centuries of progress and civilization we live in greater filth than alley cats in the slums of Calcutta. We still make open latrines of rivers from which others must draw their drinking water.

The pollution of disease-carrying agents is, of course, part of our sewage disposal problem. Just one cup of water taken at random from the Connecticut River, near Hartford, recently was found to contain twenty-six different infectious bacteria typically transmitted through human wastes. This condition, multiplied by several thousand similar situations in several thousand different localities, forms a very serious threat to our national health.

Pollution by synthetic-organic chemicals is almost entirely a post-World War II problem. Our national production in this area has increased 90 per cent in the past twenty years; it includes plastics, synthetic rubbers, synthetic detergents, dyes, adhesives, surface coatings, etc., and, of course, insecticides and other agricultural chemicals.

These synthetics are almost all insoluble in water and impervious to present techniques in water purification. Indeed, some actually foul the purifying process so thoroughly as to make it only minimally effective in treating other forms of pollution.

There are more than forty-five thousand pesticide formulae now registered with the U.S. Department of Agriculture. About 800 million pounds of these deadly synthetics are purchased each year and they are distributed over 30 million acres of cropland. (The usage is expected to rise 1,000 per cent before 1980.) A great portion of this material, much of it swept off the land and other surfaces and carried along by the rainfall, eventually finds its way into the nation's waterways. So does a great portion of the 25,317,000 tons of fertilizer which we put each year on our fields and gardens.

It has been proved that these substances have a very deleterious effect on fish and other wildlife. It seems logically obvious that they must also have a damaging effect on human life.

A little discussed but important form of pollution is heat, which is pretty much in a category of its own.

When the temperature increases in a stream, the amount of

141

oxygen which can be held in solution decreases. This makes the water less capable of fulfilling its natural function of decomposition and purification, and pollution increases.

Heat pollution occurs mainly when water, used to cool industrial and power-plant operations, is returned to the streams. The returning water is far warmer than it was when it left the stream, and it has a strong effect on the temperature of the stream as a whole. There are other causes of increased water heat in our rivers, such as increased power navigation, and the impoundment of water for dams (since still water is warmer than flowing water). They all add up to another important element in a serious problem.

There is no more water on the earth today than there was in the time of Adam. And despite the fact that our demands on the supply are infinitely greater than they ever have been, the amount is sufficient to sustain us—if we can learn to use it and reuse it properly. On an average day in the United States a volume of almost 5 trillion gallons of water splashes on our land in the form of rain, hail, dew, snow or sleet. Three-fourths of this rises again by evaporation, unused, into the heavens whence it came. The rest either settles into the earth or runs with our rivers.

In succeeding chapters we shall discuss various ways of using this enormous supply of water to optimum advantage: by taking it when we want it from the clouds, by desalting the seas, by storing it intelligently and by transporting it great distances so that it will be readily available in the areas that need it most.

But the major problem is how to keep our water clean in

order that it can be used and reused. This is a man-made problem and it can be solved by man.

What are we doing about it?

Relatively little. Recent legislation has pointed the way toward a solution, but there is a great deal that can and must be done before really significant improvement is made. Even the most heroic efforts to date have served merely to retard pollution, not to cure it. The Water Quality Act of 1965 goes a lot farther than previous legislation has gone, but it still falls short of what must be done.

Federal Leadership

The federal government, in this area, started out by offering too little, too late. The Water Pollution Control Act of 1948 was the first comprehensive legislation in this field, and it came at least half a century later than it should have come. Because of the solid opposition of certain industrial interests, this bill emerged as a law with very ineffective teeth. It contained neither a carrot nor a stick. The bill encouraged beneficial cooperative efforts among the states, but it did not afford much armament to be used against communities and industries which failed to comply with the recommendations of the law.

The first major legislative breakthrough came in 1956. The Congress passed a new water pollution control law, which was sponsored by Congressmen John A. Blatnik of Minnesota and Robert E. Jones of Alabama. For the first time, the federal government recognized the impelling public need by putting up matching money as an inducement to local municipalities to improve their community sewage treatment works and thus help liberate the streams from the monstrous volume of untreated and poorly treated wastes that had been flowing into them from inadequate and outmoded treatment plants.

Recognizing the formidable and in some cases prohibitive problem of financing these costly works on the limited revenues available through local taxation, the Congress decreed that—where it could be shown that an efficient, modern disposal plant would contribute materially to freeing a stream from pollution—the federal government would match up to 30 per cent of the construction cost. For this specific purpose, Congress authorized appropriations of $50 million a year. Coming to only about thirty cents per citizen annually on a per capita basis, this amount was far from enough. But it was indeed enough to make a long overdue start.

In an effort to assure that the limited funds would be spread around over the entire country and thus extend their potential benefits widely throughout the land, Congress provided in this 1956 law that no more than $250,000 could be granted to any individual project. This restriction proved to be both a strength and a weakness. It did indeed stimulate badly needed activity in an enormous number of localities, but the ceiling on individual grants made the incentive less than effective for the larger cities where the gravest problems exist.

The bill itself was passed only after a bitter debate. Harking back to ancient dogma, some railed that it was a "boondoggle," a "give-away," an "unwarranted invasion of local responsibility." Critics argued that it would do "more harm than good." Their doctrinaire rhetoric went this way: The lure of federal money would actually slow down construction of sewage plants by discouraging cities from developing the "initiative" to build plants on their own and enticing them to wait until each could be certified in turn for a federal "handout."

The experience of the program, happily, proved the critics wrong. In the first three years following enactment, construction of new sewage treatment works throughout the nation almost doubled the pace of the preceding three-year period. In increasing numbers, cities were moving ahead—on their own where possible, with federal help where necessary. In many cases, the matching grants made the decisive difference in a town's financial capacity to launch the needed improvement.

The 1956 law also provided for intensified research to determine the health effects of new pollutants, technical assistance to states and a program of demonstrations and training.

The program was working. But it still was a bit like dabbing iodine on a broken toe. Other legislative innovations were superimposed upon the pilot program to make it more effective. In 1961, amendments to this basic law increased the annual authorization, raised the dollar ceiling for a single project from $250,000 to $600,000 and encouraged cooperative projects to serve two or more cities. As an inducement for communities to get together on larger projects, it was agreed that several municipalities building one adequate plant for their joint use could offset the larger cost by claiming the amounts individually accruing to each—up to a maxi-

mum of $2.4 million for a giant unified project involving eight
or more cities.

During the first eight years of this program's operation, it
had directly encouraged the building of 5,994 modern purification plants in communities throughout the country. Approximately $500 million in federal grants had stimulated
local investments of more than $3 billion in water purity.

Impressive as this was, it still wasn't enough. The rapid
proliferation of increasing contamination of our streams had
been halted, but, from the standpoint of the pollution *level*,
we were just about standing still. The infection had ceased
to spread dangerously throughout the body of our nation's
rivers, but the *degree* of infection was just about the same.
While we were eradicating old sources of pollution, new
sources were springing up through the growth of industry
and population density. We had begun to hold own own. We
were not, however, making appreciable headway on a national basis.

Yet the program had been sufficiently successful that
Congressional opposition, at first rabid, had just about died
out entirely. By 1965, when the Congress broadened and expanded the antipollution fight, this new bill produced in the
House the extremely rare phenomenon of an unanimous vote
—395 to 0. So sharply did this contrast with the acrimonious
fight and the relatively close margin (213 to 165) which
launched the national campaign to abate stream contamination nine years earlier, that it establishes beyond doubt the
belated awareness of the national lawmaking body to the
gravely serious nature of the problem.

The Water Quality Act of 1965 not only builds upon the

successful experience of the 1956 law but branches out into several new fronts in our continuing fight to pass on to the American posterity a heritage of clean water.

Research grants comprise one forward-looking aspect of the program. Two centers are nearing completion. Oil and chemical companies and detergent and pesticide firms, spurred by public opinion, are joining to spend millions in studies looking to improved techniques which can protect streams that once ran sparkling clear from being further clogged by toxic industrial wastes.

More money was made available for the practical battle to clean up the streams. The new bill authorizes $150 million a year in federal matching assistance to municipalities and water districts for purifying discharges into the streams. This still amounts to less than one dollar per year for each citizen —to preserve the one commodity without which no citizen can live. But it is three times what we started with, just nine years before.

States are encouraged to get into the act. Ceilings on individual grants to big metropolitan cities where most of the pollution originates (earlier pegged at $600,000) will be raised to a full 30 per cent, regardless of the total cost, if the states will match the federal funds.

Better administration, too, will result from the upgrading of pollution control from a division within a bureau of the Public Health Service within the Department of Health, Education, and Welfare, and from the consolidation of many scattered activities under one effective head. And enforcement against willful polluters will have to become a reality. But the matter of water quality standards is left to the states,

147

each of which is asked to develop a set of water-quality criteria and to embark in the next two years upon a program of local enforcement.

This later provision was a compromise between the House and Senate versions of the bill. The Senate, led in this matter by Senator Edmund Muskie of Maine, wanted to require federal standards immediately. This had evoked anguished outcries from many of the states. State water authorities almost unanimously protested that they were making some appreciable headway in requiring industries to treat their wastes, but feared the effects of a single federal standard. The Congress ultimately decreed in the 1965 law, however, that federal mandatory standards would have to come by 1967.

The total amount of money involved in this struggle still probably is far from enough to do the job that needs doing. Governor Nelson Rockefeller of New York appeared before our House Committee during the hearings and argued eloquently that at least $250 million a year was needed on the part of the federal government. There will be more on his testimony, later in this chapter.

In the Committee report on the Water Quality Act of 1965 appear these words:

The impact of the Federal Water Pollution Control Act has been impressive. It has taken us less than nine years from a situation in which untrammeled pollution threatened to foul the Nation's waterways beyond hope of restoration, to a point where we are holding our own. But that is not enough. The unprecedented and continuing population and economic growth are imposing ever-increasing demands upon our available water supplies. The accompanying trends toward increased urbanization and marked technological change create new and complex water quality problems, further diminishing available water supplies. . . . The Committee believes [S. 4, the bill in question] . . . is a further and necessary step in continuing efforts to bring about proper water pollution control and a full upgrading of the water quality of our streams, rivers and lakes.

The new law creates a Federal Water Pollution Control Administration under the Department of Health, Education, and Welfare, which will be in charge of all federal antipollution activities. It also authorizes a four-year program with an annual level of $20 million for grants to develop new and improved methods of controlling waste discharges in those older communities which still combine storm sewers and sanitary sewers in a single system of conduits, mingling organic wastes with rainfall.

The act also doubles the dollar ceiling for the construction of individual waste treatment works, from $600,000 to $1.2 million, and from $2.4 million to $4.8 million for a joint project.

It is a good law, a strong step forward. It will go a considerable distance in the fight against pollution. It may even permit us to make progress in the war against water contamination, rather than just mark time as we have been doing. But it is a far from perfect bill. Before we can say we have this problem whipped we must be prepared to spend a great deal more money than we have authorized to date, and we must also be prepared to put sharp teeth into the law which will permit the federal government to force compliance when voluntary compliance, after all other efforts have failed, still is not forthcoming.

The Congress, the Executive and the people must realize

that the job of facing up to the water pollution problem is far from over. There is no easy solution, no one-shot cure. We must be prepared to undertake a continuing program of construction of purifying plants and massive, covered trunk-sewer systems, research and development in purifying techniques, policing our rivers and lakes and conducting a long-range educational course for the public on the subject of pollution.

Obviously, all of this cannot be accomplished in just one bill, or in just one year. But we must not falter; to date, even our best efforts are only retarding pollution, not eliminating it. And federal action alone cannot do the job. Every level of organized society must be enlisted in the battle.

Experiment on the Ohio

A constructive cooperative assault on the problem has been made on the troublesome and very troubled Ohio River. It is possibly the most notable of several similar group efforts being made to control pollution, to treat water not only at intake, but before output, and to reduce significantly the degree of contamination in the sewage that is sent floating down the stream.

The Ohio River Valley Water Sanitation Commission (known as ORSANCO) was formed in 1949 with the approval of Congress. It is an interstate agency, and the Governors of Ohio, Kentucky, Pennsylvania, Illinois, Indiana, Virginia, West Virginia and New York signed the original compact which brought it into being in Cincinnati on June 30, 1948.

This is an effort that should have begun a half-century earlier, but, at least, it represents a solid, healthy effort at massive cooperation to solve an overwhelming problem. Let me say cautiously that ORSANCO is not yet an unqualified success. There are critics who point out that the pollution of the Ohio River is greater today than it was on the day ORSANCO was founded. In reply, I would ask that one imagine what the conditions *would* have been had *not* a broad and concentrated program been undertaken in the first place. I will let the reader decide for himself the answer to that question by pointing out a few of the many accomplishments of the group.

A preamble to the agreement declares that each state is prepared to pledge to every other "faithful cooperation in the control of future pollution and in the abatement of existing pollution from the rivers, streams, and waters in the Ohio River Basin which flow through, into or border upon any of such signatory States."

Thus an attempt was undertaken to halt what had become a serious deterioration in the thousand-mile Ohio River, one of the main arteries of commerce in the United States, with more than 3½ million persons living along its shores. The guiding principles of the agreement, with eight states pledging themselves to a common front against a common problem, gave to those working on the project the zeal of crusaders. In any such program, public opinion and support is an absolutely necessary ingredient for success. For once, political communities, far removed from others downstream, were induced to consider the effect their actions had on these remote areas.

A new sense of community and regional obligation was apparent.

The effectiveness of the cooperation extended by all parties can be judged by the fact that within the first fifteen years of its existence, only six times have the enforcement provisions of the agreement been brought into play in this geographic area involving hundreds of municipalities and industries. State after state passed or strengthened its legislation, giving legal teeth to the detailed contract signed by the chief executives. Industry, one of the prime contributors to pollution, was fully represented in the planning activities of the group, and extended remarkable cooperation on the whole. Public opinion soon began to demand it.

During the first days of ORSANCO almost every newspaper, radio station and television station within the area joined in a campaign to explain the reasons for the organization. They exposed some of the deplorable conditions prevailing in the river basin, much of which was news to most people. Civic organizations, service clubs, chambers of commerce and professional groups all put their weight behind the program.

Just how bad things were at the time the Commission began its work was revealed in testimony by Edward J. Cleary, executive director and chief engineer of ORSANCO. Appearing before the Natural Resources and Power Subcommittee of the House in June 1963, he told of conditions just fifteen years ago along the once "beautiful Ohio."

"In 1948 less than 1 per cent of the 3½ million people living in communities along the river provided treatment for their sewage discharges," he said. "The industrial record was equally depressing. . . . It reflected a lack of citizen under-standing, and with it a lack of leadership."

Understanding and leadership were partly supplied by the campaign conducted by press, radio, television and civic groups to build public support and instigate public action.

Cleary added: "The theme has been: Persuasion if possi-ble, but compulsion where necessary." Did this work out? At the time of his testimony more than 97 per cent of the population along the Ohio River was being served with sew-age treatment facilities. So, obviously, public attitudes had changed considerably, and in a way which meant support for huge outlays of bond and tax revenues to do the job. This accomplishment indicates that a half-century tradition of indifference can be reversed.

In addition to creating a spirit of cooperation on the part of everyone along the river, ORSANCO, although on a mod-est budget, has had a continuous research program underway, seeking ways to eliminate such things as phenol pollution, usually related to steel production.

A surveillance and monitoring system is operated by par-ticipating members, and information on the water quality of the entire length of the river is registered continuously on a twenty-four-hour-a-day basis. These data are forwarded elec-tronically to ORSANCO headquarters in Cincinnati where all conditions in the river system are noted. Unusual changes brought about by specific contaminating occurrences can be spotted and kept under surveillance, and corrective action is employed where required. These electronic guardians have done their job well.

Such alerts have had their use in other ways, too. Not too

long ago, a truck filled with cyanide overturned and fell into the river some fourteen miles upstream from Louisville, on the Indiana side. Robot monitors on the river immediately flashed indications of the sudden change in the water due to the presence of this deadly poison. All communications media in Louisville did an excellent job of alerting the populace to the danger, disseminating reliable information and eliminating the danger of panic.

Fortunately, no damage was done, except to fish in the area. The monitoring system kept reporting that the poisonous substance was being diluted rapidly. So quickly did this occur that by the time the streamflow reached Louisville, not a trace was reported by the monitors. True, as it turned out, there was no danger to the residents of the city. But since they knew this for actual fact, the danger of hysteria was eliminated. For no other reason than that, the monitoring system was worth its cost.

All this would indicate that great strides have been made in cleaning up the Ohio River and its tributaries. There can be no question that ORSANCO represents one of the best, if not the best, antipollution compacts in the country. An improvement from 100 per cent *untreated* sewage sixteen years ago to nearly 100 per cent *treated* sewage today speaks for itself. More than 90 per cent of the industrial plants discharging wastes into the river and its tributaries are complying with at least the minimum requirements laid down by the agency. More than a billion dollars in public funds were spent by thirteen hundred communities for sewage treatment facilities throughout the drainage basin. Private industry has spent about a half-billion dollars for treatment of industrial waste. Impressive figures and statistics, those.

But ORSANCO is not without its critics, and some of the criticism is valid. The Ohio River still is rated as a highly polluted stream. Although most communities are in agreement with the grand scheme, there are others which still spoil the waters with untreated wastes; and there are two hundred or more nonparticipating industries which add their filth to the stream, thus making it impossible for the task ever to be completed successfully.

Additionally, some authorities charge the criteria for industry are too low. If the cooperating industries just barely qualify, they are not really doing enough to alleviate the problem. Also, with no legal power to force companies to reveal pollution data, and, indeed, with state laws protecting the companies from being made to do so, an inventory of their polluting activities is not of sufficient depth to be of much actual use in the fight. The legislature of Ohio, the state which was responsible more than any other for the formation of ORSANCO, has tied that body's hands in this important respect, by law.

Proponents of ORSANCO rebut these arguments by saying that the guidelines first established are, in a sense, merely a beginning, a minimum set of standards to cut down on the pollutants being introduced into the various rivers of the basin. Once this stage has been completed, then a stepped-up program will get underway which eventually will clean up all the streams once and for all, and will keep them that way.

Each position is a valid one. Great accomplishments have been registered. Greater ones are needed. In any event I shudder to think what conditions on the Ohio would be today, if ORSANCO had not been created.

If this valiant attempt is only a beginning, and it is still young at age sixteen, we can well imagine what we are faced with across this nation, if every river basin is to undergo a similarly comprehensive program to eliminate the economically destructive and unhealthy scourge of pollution.

One State's Battle Plan

If the heads of the Ohio River Sanitation Commission can point with pride to the $1 billion dollars of public funds expended in a period of sixteen years in the pollution war, they will have to take a backseat when Governor Nelson A. Rockefeller of New York opens his campaign in the fight. Should every governor of every state face up to planning a coordinated assault on pollution as has the New York State Chief Executive, we would have our battle plan drawn, our forces ready, and victory would be a predictable conclusion.

Appearing before the Public Works Committee of the House of Representatives on February 23, 1965, the Governor outlined a program of water pollution control proposed by his state. It captured the imaginations of all of us who heard him. Rockefeller is launching a whopping $1.7-billion program spread over a six-year period. He summarized the water situation as it concerned the state of New York and explained what was needed to overcome it and what he proposed to do about it. Many others had been before the committee, but none before had laid it on the line so well, particularly in regard to dollars to be spent, and the time element needed to lick a major part of the problem.

Governor Rockefeller identified water as the "common

denominator" of economic growth, and the growing demand for pure water as "our number one problem."

His statement evidenced not only vision but also a certain amount of political courage. He had been for some time under attack for having raised tax rates throughout his state, increases which, he said, must be made if New York was to meet its responsibilities to its citizens. Now he was ready to stand up for an additional outlay of funds, very little of which would come from the federal program. He argued for a more liberal matching arrangement than current legislation permits, recommending that a third of the total amount to be spent be furnished by the U.S. government, as against less than 5 per cent under present law. But he fully accepted the fact that a greater amount of funding for the municipalities would have to come from Albany.

In illustration of New York's problem, he pointed out that more than 87 per cent of the state's population is urban in character and that 75 per cent are living in areas where pollution is an extremely serious problem.

Selecting but a handful of the projects listed in the New York plan, the Governor revealed immediate requirements for the expenditure of more than $170 million for sewage treatment plants in New York City, Troy, Albany, Nassau County, Westchester County, Suffolk County and the Rockland Sewer District. There was no point in not doing all the work in concert, he explained, since no city downstream wants to pour money into a sewage treatment system when their neighbors upstream continue to pollute the river passing by their doorstep.

As proposed by Governor Rockefeller, the state would

157

furnish 30 per cent of the costs, across the board, with the U.S. government adding a like amount. Authorization for a billion-dollar bond issue to finance the state's participation would be asked of the voters. Additionally, tax benefits for industry, with possible furnishing of low-cost loans as well, would be proposed. These arrangements would be intended to give industry added incentive for doing all it can to eliminate its own pollution activities, beyond the minimums currently required under law.

He advocated a close working partnership among federal, state and local agencies in completing monitoring systems for all waterways and expansion of research and promised vigorous state law-enforcement, adopting those criteria laid down by Health, Education, and Welfare Department experts as a yardstick for measuring compliance.

The voters of New York State in November of 1965 overwhelmingly endorsed their governor's plan. By a 4–1 vote, they approved a $1 billion bond issue to build sewage treatment facilities. This margin of taxpayer support was historically unprecedented in the state for such a vast spending program.

The master plan, ambitiously designed to clean up the water resources of the state within the next six years, calls for a sweeping construction program of interceptor sewers and treatment plants. The state will pay 30 per cent, and where necessary will pre-finance the federal government's 30 per cent matching share, leaving only the remaining 40 per cent of the cost to be picked up by the municipal governments.

Additionally, as a stimulus to local governmental units and individual industries, the state-imposed debt limit on local government bonds for this purpose is lifted, and industry is to receive a real property tax exemption and a one-year depreciation write-off against corporate franchise taxes for monies spent on waste treatment facilities.

The enthusiastic response of New York voters provides convincing proof that the American people will support a bold and imaginative program for pure water when it is properly presented. The Rockefeller plan had been endorsed by both major political parties in the state. It was actively supported by the League of Women Voters and by an impressive array of civic, business and educational organizations throughout the state.

Commenting on the New York plan, Congressman John A. Blatnik, acting Committee Chairman at the time, and one of the nations leading authorities on water, said ". . . This is certainly a constructive, bold and sweeping, head-on approach, and obviously a very well considered approach, to meet the problem."

Blatnik's statement reflected the opinion of most of us who listened to Governor Rockefeller that February day. Every state needs to launch such a head-on attack.

Resurrection of a River

Another hopeful example of massive community action has been the reversal of the pronounced death trend of New Jersey's Raritan River. At one time this stream was one of the most beautiful in the United States, a popular site for swimming meets. It abounded with shellfish, shad and other marine life. In those days they called it fondly "Queen of

Rivers." Even up to World War I, its water was clear and fresh and pleasant-tasting. Within a short time after that war, the pollution level had reached such a state that aquatic contestants refused to perform in its foul waters. The public shunned it. The fishing industry was all but dead, with one of the finest oyster beds in the world so contaminated it was no longer of use.

This sad state of affairs was brought on by the rapid industrialization of the Raritan Valley and its corresponding population expansion. More than 350 industrial plants now nestle along the hundred-mile river, about eight times the total at the turn of the century. For years wastes from these varied industries were poured into the river by the billions of gallons, commingling with untreated wastes from municipalities.

Eventually the river became one mass of filthy sludge, a jammed conduit of contamination and corruption which killed off the fish, closing down a thriving industry. The stench along its course was unbearable, and the health problem had become alarming. By 1930, the river was considered to be one of the most contaminated streams in the country. Bacteria counts had reached nearly a hundred times the level considered minimally safe. By the mid-1930's there seemed little or no hope that the river could be saved.

Then, and only then, did several of the municipalities and a few industries become sufficiently concerned to take action. Exhaustive studies were conducted by sanitary engineers and a series of recommendations made.

The least troublesome and easiest financed of the recommendations was that the individual communities should build treatment plants. When the federal Public Works Administration offered to furnish funds for such projects, many communities along the river accepted this solution.

Some of the communities, however, refused to participate. In addition, very few industries had their own treatment systems and the others were supremely indifferent to the problem. In spite of the valiant efforts of the farsighted few, the contamination level rose. But, due to the good works of the few, the *rate* of rise was somewhat slower.

Then World War II came along, and with it even greater industrial expansion—and more pollution. The cause seemed irretrievably lost.

Matters became so bad that the New Jersey State Department of Health banned the construction of any plant which would require use of water from the Raritan River. What industry could exist without water? This effectively brought to a halt any further industrial expansion.

Again studies were conducted by authorities. This time more of the industries participated. Research into past recommendations revealed that the earlier engineering report had suggested the establishment of a common trunk-sewer, with a central treatment plant to process all the wastes of the Raritan Valley. This idea finally caught the imaginations of those seeking a solution, and a very intensive public education program was undertaken.

By 1951, plans were developed for an immense trunk-sewer throughout the length of the valley. Connecting lines from other portions of the area would tie into this central line. All wastes then would be carried into the central treatment plant. Upon completion of treatment, solubles would be pumped two miles out into Raritan Bay. Those solids that

161

could not be broken down were to be carried out miles to sea by barges, and discharged into the Atlantic Ocean.

To sell the program, industries sponsored a film depicting the horrors of the Raritan River and showing the recommended solution. Some of the horror scenes were so vivid that viewers were sickened. Newspapers, radio and television stations joined in the campaign to save the river. Public opinion was aroused. Local authorities, feeling they were doing all that was required on an independent basis, were being prodded to commit their communities to the basin-wide scheme. Some officials were reluctant to do so because of investments already made in local treatment plants. Even though the plants were by then overloaded, the communities were loath to spend more money on decontamination.

A solution for this problem was finally conceived by the Middlesex County Sewerage Authority, the organization created to establish, and be responsible for, the system. Funds were to be raised through the sale of bonds, without taxing the communities. Those communities joining the sewer plan would be compensated for their useless treatment plants. The cost of building and operating a single system would be much cheaper than for the many separate systems—an economy that would be reflected in tax savings throughout the valley. Furthermore, improvement and maintenance costs of these separate treatment plants would be eliminated.

Although not all communities and industries joined the plan, enough of them participated to permit the system to begin operation in 1958. Within months, the Raritan began to show definite improvement. Thousands of tons of sludge on the bottom of the river were broken up, dissolved, and washed to sea, as the now running waters could begin the purification action which is inherent in freely flowing streams. Fish began to return to the river.

The Raritan River has improved measurably over its former condition. Again it has the breath of life. But with several communities and large industries going their own way, the fight for total recovery cannot be completely won. Constant vigilance by the State Board of Health of these nonmembers will be required so long as they remain aloof from the system. Also the continuing growth of both population and industrial expansion requires enlargement of the authority's facilities. And Raritan Bay still has to be smelled to be believed.

Nevertheless, this is an example of collective action bringing a dead river back to life. The day may come when New Jerseyites once again can refer to the Raritan as the "Queen of Rivers."

A few isolated success stories should not allow us to become overly optimistic. Experience with the Ohio and Raritan Rivers can point the way to similar action for other parts of the country. These efforts have not yet solved the pollution problem. As populations grow and industry becomes more concentrated, the problem itself will become much worse, and present measures are inadequate to combat it.

One of the most knowledgeable members of Congress on water matters is the quiet, able John A. Blatnik of Minnesota. He is known as the father of our nationwide antipollution program. Speaking in Washington this year to the International Water Quality Symposium, he said this:

163

Is America really suffering a water shortage? The answer is "No." Our country is suffering from one hundred years of mismanagement, waste, devastation and neglect of its water sources. . . . But there is no shortage of water anywhere in the United States except in the traditionally arid sections of the West. . . . What we are suffering is a very real shortage of *usable water!*

Senator Harrison A. Williams of New Jersey told a Senate Subcommittee on Pollution recently:

When foam starts coming out of the water faucet, when septic tanks begin polluting underground water supplies, when beaches are closed, when cases of hepatitis begin to break out and the fishing industry is crippled, I say it's time for some real action in the field of water pollution.

I'll go along with John Blatnik and "Pete" Williams.

But we all had better start going along soon, and fast.

By 1970, American industry will be dumping into our streams and lakes the equivalent in filth of the untreated wastes of 210 million people. This will be in addition to the human wastes that 59 million Americans are already slopping into the watercourses through primitive and inadequate sewer systems.

The United States of America cannot continue to bumble along, trying to ignore this critical situation until a deadly outbreak of cholera, or some other plague, sweeps over several of our states.

Surely we do not need a disaster to bring us to our senses.

Surely we have learned *something* from history.

7 From the Hills

"To rule the mountains is to rule the river."
—Old Chinese Proverb

Mention a federal water-development program and most people instantly conjure up a mental image of a big, famous project like Hoover Dam.

This is natural, I suppose, but these major installations are only a part of the federal government's program to conserve and develop our national water resources.

It's true, of course, that gargantuan dams like Hoover and Oroville are vital to our present and future. These vast projects are built mostly by the Bureau of Reclamation and the U.S. Army Corps of Engineers, and they do a good and necessary job of serving the people and protecting the land *below* them.

But what protects the areas *above* them? And what protects *them?*

If these grandiose projects are to remain and continue to serve future generations, we must supplement and protect them from the ravages of sedimentation and siltation. To do this, we must hold the land in place above them. This can be done by good planting practices, by cover crops, by terraces and levees, and by the construction of small dams and reservoirs up in the little watersheds in the hills and highlands, for here are the sources of the tributaries that form the great rivers.

As a matter of fact, unless we do carry the idea of water preservation to its logical conclusion, many of the great dams we have built will eventually become next to useless because the silt buildup behind them will have reduced the storage capacity of the reservoirs they recreated to a small fraction of that which was deemed necessary in the first place.

One of the most common causes of water waste and land loss in this country is the flash flood. These floods have tormented large areas of the nation ever since people began to settle alongside rivers.

These floods typically occur when a prolonged, torrential downpour follows a significant period of drought. The water is not absorbed into the parched and cracked earth. It runs off, taking with it tons of precious topsoil which nature had required literally centuries to create. When the silt-laden water, in its riotous course, reaches the streams already choked by innumerable invasions of this kind over the years, it causes these streams to burst out of their banks and to inflict irreparable damage upon the countryside for miles around.

When the waters recede they leave behind them a residue of death, ruined homesteads, desolated crops and ravished hopes.

In some areas today, flooding occurs far less frequently than it once did, and, when it does occur, it causes far less damage. The credit for this improvement belongs in large part to a very important and farseeing piece of legislation:

the Watershed Protection and Flood Prevention Act of 1954, or, as it is more prosaically called, Public Law 566.

The purpose of this program is to attack the flooding problem at its source, up in the highlands, along the creek banks in the thousands of little waterheds where the tributaries of the great rivers begin. The law authorizes the treatment of these smaller watersheds through the construction of soil conservation dams, and by widening and deepening the channels of potentially fractious streams. It insists upon state and local participation, and it encourages individual farmers to undertake programs of contour planting and terracing and to establish cover crops which literally hold the land down and thus prevent the excessive siltation which is a major cause of serious overflowing.

When we talk of soil conservation dams, we mean structures costing a few thousand dollars, rather than millions, to complete. This is small potatoes when compared to such structures as the half-billion dollar Oroville Dam in California, but, as we shall see, the complex of small reservoirs on the tributaries is necessary not only for the protection of the land and the good they achieve in their immediate upstream localities but for the protection they provide for our investments along the main stems of the rivers, including the big reservoirs themselves.

Public Law 566 received its first significant test in mid-spring of 1957, three years after its passage. For seven years the Southwest had suffered from a severe drought. The long parching had affected the agricultural economy of the area drastically. The drought was so prolonged and intense that, in some places, measurements showed the earth to be powder-dry to the depth of twelve feet and more.

Then at last, the rains came. Suddenly. Not only did they come; they persisted. For more than six weeks the area was drenched, and recordings of thirteen and fourteen inches in a day were not uncommon. The average rainfall for the Great Plains area, in some localities, was 500 per cent of normal. In just six weeks, more than 145 *trillion* gallons of water were dumped on the States of Texas and Oklahoma. This adds up to 445 million acres of land covered to a depth of one foot.

The effect of the deluge was disastrous. The powder-dry earth turned to a kind of a muddy *bouillabaisse* and was carried off by the water to do damage wherever it went. However, the extent of the damage differed widely between those areas which had been able to take advantage of the provisions of Public Law 566, and those that had not.

I remember vividly the tragedy that was enacted in Lampasas and Burnet Counties, which lie somewhat to the south and west of Forth Worth, in my own state of Texas.

After three weeks of almost incessant but fairly gentle rain, these two counties were hit on May 12, 1957, by a cloudburst which flung down a torrent of ten inches in a few hours. The streams, already swollen, roared out of their banks and forcefully attacked the communities in their vicinity. Houses were reduced to kindling in a matter of minutes; automobiles were almost literally torn apart. Five persons in Lampasas were drowned; 430 families were rendered homeless. More than 168 business and industrial establishments—a major portion of the downtown sections of the small communities involved— were wrecked. The dollar value of the damage in the locality was set at approximately $6.5 million, an estimate that many consider to be on the conservative side.

Ironically, engineering designs of a watershed plan for the area had been completed and authorized in February, 1957, three months before the catastrophe struck. This was too late, of course, to be of any use in this crisis because the construction had not been completed before the deluge came.

Spurred on by the horror that occurred, Congress rushed through appropriations for an accelerated watershed control program in the Lampasas area, which the engineers completed in two years. When another potentially fatal downpour hit the sector on June 23, 1959, the three new dams held fast and there was virtually no damage.

Although the watershed protection program throughout the Great Plains area had not advanced sufficiently by the spring of 1957 to make much of a dent in the overall damage (estimated at around $200 million), nevertheless sufficient data emerged to prove its potential worth. More than 800,000 acres of cultivated land unprotected by the Small Watershed program suffered fertile soil damage averaging almost 80 per cent of the value of the land. Where the small watershed programs had been completed, fertile soil damage averaged less than 5 per cent. Two counties in the Ouachita River Basin in Oklahoma, which were protected by the new program, suffered total damages of only $4,700. Only ninety-four acres in the entire two counties were flooded!

There had been many skeptics about the usefulness of Public Law 566 before the floods of 1957. There were few afterward.

A similarly dramatic proof of the efficacy of the program

occurred in South Central Ohio in the early spring of 1963. A heavy rain of about 3.4 inches cascaded onto land that was still solidly frozen to a depth of 26 inches. The water, naturally, ran off immediately, following the course of least resistance, causing havoc wherever it went. The nearby communities—except for the town of Lancaster—were severely damaged. In one community alone the damage was estimated at half a million dollars.

However, Lancaster and its surrounding farm area had previously participated in the building of the Upper Hocking Watershed Project. In this protected watershed, eight small upstream dams held back 325 million gallons of water. Lancaster and its farmland suffered practically no damage. If it had *not* been for the watershed project, at least two feet of floodwater and silt would have attacked the town, causing hundreds of thousands of dollars in damages.

The road to soil and water conservation has been a long one. It has been traveled by sporadic outbursts of energy. The history of conservation legislation dates back to 1891 when the first national forest reserves were created. One of the reasons officially cited was "the securing of favorable conditions of waterflows." The intolerable conditions which lay in the wake of the dust bowls of the 1930's, brought about a public demand for conservation programs. A series of sporadic laws attempted to cope with the problem.

The Watershed Protection and Flood Prevention Act of 1954 was at the time of its enactment the most significant and far-reaching piece of legislation of this kind in our history. It was the joint, bipartisan creation of two genuine, certifiable agricultural *statesmen* in the Congress, Representatives W. R. Poage (Democrat, Texas) and Clifford R. Hope

(Republican, Kansas), and it broke entirely new ground in several important respects.

Public Law 566 was the first *small* watershed legislation ever to be enacted, and despite the fact that many amendments have been added since 1954, it still remains the basic authority under which all such programs are carried out today. The act was an innovation in that it placed the full responsibility for initiating watershed projects on the local people involved, acting through their own community organizations. Whenever this was done, the program was identified as a *local* project being carried out with federal assistance, rather than as a federal undertaking.

The responsible local organization is required to share in the cost, and to operate and maintain the projects, when completed. It also is the responsibility of the local interests to acquire all the land necessary for the success of the program, and to obtain the requisite easements and rights-of-way. No land can be acquired by the federal government, and all structures involved have to be owned by the local people.

Second, the law decreed that the local organizations are responsible for developing each individual watershed plan, with federal cooperation, and have full authority to approve or disapprove. The local sponsors are charged also with the task of awarding construction contracts.

Third, the act provided that each project must be approved by the state government before it can receive federal help, and then only on a priority basis assigned by the state.

Thus the act laid heavy and healthy stress on local initiative and responsibility. It avoided the far-too-usual trap of leaving everything up to the federal government to decide, adjudicate, finance and operate.

171

The original law has been amended and strengthened since 1954. In 1956, for instance, Public Law 1018 permitted federal assistance for these watershed projects to include storage capacity in the upstream reservoirs for the development of municipal and industrial water supplies, in addition to exclusively agricultural purposes such as flood prevention and irrigation. This has proven to be a major step forward.

The Food and Agriculture Act of 1962 (Public Law 703) included recreational purposes in the federal cost-sharing program. This modification also permitted the cost-sharing to be established on a total program basis, instead of being limited just to individual projects. Most important, it made possible the inclusion of water-storage projects for *future* municipal and industrial use, with repayment and interest charges deferred up to ten years.

Not unnaturally, most states have responded enthusiastically to this legislation, and their legislatures have passed enabling bills of their own, permitting full participation in the program. Almost three hundred laws have been passed in forty-three states, so far, facilitating a truly workable partnership between the U.S. Department of Agriculture, the state governments and local authorities.

The overall program is soundly based from a legislative point of view. It is geared for success. It is working well. Public Law 566 has become one of the strongest tools we have in the water-resource development field. It has won almost universal acceptance, and the enthusiasm for its potential is growing with each passing year. No national conservation project in our history has received such widespread public support.

172

The demand, in fact, has far outpaced our actual performance. In ten years, we have developed 635 watersheds by means of this program. In June of 1965, however, there were 2,317 pending applications on file from as many scattered localities, proposing cooperative local-federal programs to develop individual watersheds covering a total of 166 million acres of land.

As evidence of the widespread popularity of this program, 143 community applications have come from Kentucky, 131 from Georgia, 129 from Texas, 103 from Oklahoma, 83 from Arkansas and 77 from Indiana. Other states, slower at first to grasp the potential, now are beginning to flood the Department with applications. Up to this point, Texas leads the nation in project approvals (with 43), followed by Oklahoma (36), Georgia (33), Arkansas (27), North Carolina (26) and Iowa (26).

In the 635 projects already undertaken, the major structural works include 3,836 single-purpose floodwater-retarding reservoirs, 1,363 grade-stabilization structures, 210 multipurpose reservoirs, 29 other single-purpose reservoirs and 9,459 miles of channel improvement.

The total cost of the first 500 approved projects, in nine years of construction, runs to $743 million. Of this sum, the federal share is $441 million, and the nonfederal share $302 million. The nonfederal portion breaks down into about $197 million borne by farmers and landowners for individual land treatment measures such as terraces, and $105 million paid by local public bodies for land acquisition costs, easements, rights-of-way, administering contracts and maintaining the structures.

173

A less tangible, but perhaps almost equally important subsidiary development has been that Public Law 566 has created among both urban and rural authorities in many areas the *habit* of sitting down around the conference table to discuss and solve mutual problems.

The program, if carried through on a sufficient scale, will eventually rid most of the country of the fear of floods, erosion and siltation. It will substantially reduce the risk of farming. It also will lower the maintenance costs of roads and bridges, as well as free urban communities of the responsibility for such costly and repetitive disasters as that which devastated Lampasas, Texas, and countless other communities throughout the country. These beneficial effects already are being felt wherever projects have been completed.

But all this actually is only part of the story. Many times these projects yield important fringe benefits by stimulating the economies of their communities. During fiscal 1965 alone, twenty-eight of our states contributed more than $2.2 million of their own funds for planning projects under the program, and twenty states spent a total of almost $10 million for improvements on projects already in existence.

The effect on the economy was remarkable—especially in depressed areas. Jobs were created, the standard of living was raised, and rural poverty was eased. In short, the communities got a real economic shot in the arm.

Consider the case of Culpeper, a town of twenty-four hundred persons in northern Virginia. The Mountain Run project, in that area, not only has eliminated the danger of floods which had plagued its existence, but has assured the community of an adequate and stable water supply. Since the project was completed in 1962, three new industries, employing five hundred workers, have been attracted to the town. A community hospital, which had been held up because of the lack of reliable water supply, has been built and is now in full operation. The payroll of the three industries and the hospital comes to almost $2 million a year. Culpeper got a new lease on life.

During the 1964 drought, other communities in the vicinity, which had not participated in the watershed program, suffered severe shortages and had to ration water. Culpeper, with a 163-million-gallon reservoir, had water to spare. If all goes well, the other communities will have their own projects in the near future.

Another illustrative example is that of the Sixmile Creek project in western Arkansas. It was completed in 1955, minimizing the danger of drought and flood. Since then, this sparsely settled area has seen four industries, employing 650 people, and with an annual payroll of more than a million dollars, spring up in its midst. What's more, damage from flood and sediment in the area has been decreased, on the average, by more than forty-five thousand dollars a year, Department of Agriculture researchers have estimated.

The benefits from such programs are not confined to the immediate vicinities in which the projects are located. By treating the headwaters of streams and stopping sediment at its source, the projects greatly reduce the amount of eroded soil materials which otherwise would find their way to larger lakes downstream.

The Garza-Little Elm Reservoir, on the Elm Fork of the Trinity River in North Texas, is a case in point. Completed

175

by the Army Corps of Engineers in November of 1954, Garza-Little Elm has created a lake spanning 39,140 acres. The watershed area above it rolls gently upward over 1,600 square miles and is drained by five major tributary streams.

Subwatershed construction is under way on three of these tributaries. The fourth is in the planning stage, and the fifth is scheduled for consideration in the near future. It is estimated that when this network of upstream projects has been finished, it will include 207 floodwater retarding structures controlling 915 square miles of the sediment-contributing area located above the big reservoir.

Before this subsidiary program began, the annual sediment buildup in the Garza-Little Elm Reservoir was computed at 1,287 acre-feet. This means that enough dirt was flowing into the reservoir each year to cover 1,287 acres, one foot deep. This was, of course, gradually filling up the lake and reducing its capacity to store water. The upstream subsidiary projects will reduce the sediment yield by 42 per cent, increasing the useful life of the parent reservoir by more than one-third.

In assessing the worth of these smaller, upstream projects, we must remember that major downstream reservoirs are, by comparison, much more expensive, and that efficient sites for storing water are limited—indeed, often irreplaceable. Thus any measures, such as these, which prolong the life of these larger structures, are crucially important.

In this case, the big, downstream Garza-Little Elm Reservoir cost $22 million to construct. The upstream works which will add more than a third to its life of usefulness, including 127 smaller dams and floodwater-retarding structures, will be completed at a total cost of $4.8 million. By any yardstick,

176

even laying aside their primary purposes, this is a good investment.

The case of Pittsfield, in western Illinois, is another success that can be attributed to the upstream program. Like hundreds of other American communities, Pittsfield was plagued by the familiar problem of having too much water at some times, not enough at others. The city had a long history of alternating flood and drought.

Until 1961, Pittsfield depended for its water supply primarily on a small reservoir built in 1924. By 1961, this reservoir was half filled with silt. Pittsfield found itself storing vast quantities of mud in space vitally needed for good, clean water.

During the long, hot summers of 1953 and 1954, the city had to haul water about twenty miles from the Mississippi River. This was both awkward and expensive. Family water bills of thirty dollars a month were not extraordinary.

The rural and urban residents of the community got together and won approval for the Big Blue Creek watershed project. Sponsored jointly by the Pittsfield and the Pike County Soil Conservation District, the project called for upland conservation measures on farmlands to conserve water and reduce runoff. Included were two floodwater-retarding dams to catch and temporarily store the excess water that poured off ten thousand acres of neighboring farm lands during heavy rains. One dam alone, enlarged at local expense, now holds back more than a billion gallons of water for municipal and industrial use.

A new $500,000 nursing home has been built at Pittsfield, now that the water supply is stabilized, and several large housing developments are under construction. In addition, the city has bought five hundred acres of land adjacent to the project, and is developing a recreation area which, when completed, will attract more people and more dollars into the economy. In the mid-1950's Pittsfield looked as if it were on its way out as a community. Today, with adequate and dependable water, it is blossoming and growing.

Often overlooked are the leisure-time benefits these projects make possible. Since the Food and Agriculture Act, mentioned earlier, was passed in 1962, a total of fifty-five recreational developments have been authorized in fifty projects, and seventy-one additional developments have received preliminary approval. When these are completed, twelve thousand acres of water will be available for fishing and water sports and will be used by more than three million people a year.

The cost of the recreational facilities already authorized will be roughly split down the middle. The federal share will be $9,204,000; the local, $9,388,000.

One of the most successful of these projects already in operation is the Mud River watershed in Kentucky, where one of the detention reservoirs now makes an eight-hundred-acre lake. The Kentucky Department of Fish and Wildlife Resources is one of the sponsors and is managing the area for recreational purposes.

The Arkansas Game and Fish Commission is developing one of the reservoirs in the Flat Creek watershed project into a seven-hundred-acre lake. This attractive reservoir, known as Lake Charles, adjoins a twenty-seven-hundred-acre state game and fish area. It will attract thousands of visitors—some from as far away as Memphis and Little Rock.

In West Virginia, approximately a hundred thousand visitors a year are expected to enjoy the new public recreational development in the Big Ditch Run watershed project. The state's Department of Natural Resources, with federal assistance, has enlarged the lake and purchased 105 acres surrounding it. The state has also purchased, with its own funds, an additional 491 adjoining acres for a park. Swimming, boating, camping, picnicking—all the pleasures of the outdoors will be available.

Naturally, these recreational uses have not been allowed to interfere in any way with the more serious purposes of the watershed projects. They are merely attractive extras, but they have pumped new blood into the economy of many nearly forgotten sections of America, and they have enlarged the lives of many thousands of Americans.

I doubt that it would have been possible to win Congressional approval in 1954 for projects which included recreational uses. However, as the wisdom of the basic idea began proving itself over and over again, Congress became increasingly amenable to developing the full potential of the projects. As a result, all the newer projects are far more versatile, and are doing more things for more people, than the early sponsors of the program ever dreamed might someday become possible.

All this sounds encouraging. It is, in short, a success story —but only as far as it goes. Unfortunately, it doesn't go far enough. When we consider the accomplishments of the first eleven years in relation to the job still facing us, we shall understand that we have scarcely made even a good beginning.

The Department of Agriculture estimates that there are

more than a billion acres of undeveloped land in this country which can be made productive through the development of eight thousand additional watershed projects. In a short time, we shall need that land. We also need, right now, the water these projects will conserve.

So far, we have authorized upstream *planning* for only about 7 per cent of this billion-acre area. Installation work has actually started on only about 3 per cent of the acreage.

It is vital that we move much faster and deal much more boldly with this very important part of our national water problem.

A comprehensive program will be expensive. But, in the long run, it will be far cheaper to attack the problem vigorously now than to continue to nibble away at its edges. The cost of flood, sediment and other measurable damage in the small watershed areas continues to mount. So does the steady and irreparable loss of the nation's topsoil. So, incidentally, does the cost of performing the work.

How much is this delay costing us?

Recently the Department of Agriculture's Soil Conservation Service made a survey of 473 small watersheds containing less than 250,000 acres each. On the basis of this study, it placed the total average loss from upstream floods, in the forty-eight mainland states, at more than a billion dollars a year.

These upstream floods, unlike those in the larger water arteries, occur almost every year. Even a storm of short duration will cause a flood. A rapid snow-melt will inundate the area. So will a rain of moderate intensity, if it keeps up for any length of time. True, these floods usually don't last very long. The crest rises and falls rapidly. Sometimes they last for only a few hours. It is rare that they last a full week. But each flood causes damage, accelerates erosion, impoverishes more of the land and adds to the siltation of the larger streams.

Many distinguished authorities believe that the small watersheds may form the most important segment of the surface of our land. They provide the water supplies for a large percentage of the irrigated farmlands of the West, as well as for thousands of towns and small cities.

Most drainage needs in the East are confined to small watersheds, and the bulk of our erosion problems can be effectively solved only by public action on these crucial areas.

Of the annual billion-dollar loss we suffer from the upstream floods, 45 per cent is attributable to crop damage. Another 8 per cent comes through the loss of buildings, livestock, fences, stored crops and farm machinery.

The nonagricultural damage is also extensive. About 18 per cent of the total affects city areas, including such facilities as highways, railroads and power lines. Another 12 per cent comes from erosion—scouring the flood plain, chewing away the banks of streams and biting out ugly gullies. The rest of the damage is "indirect"—delaying the marketing of products, interrupting farm work and forcing the evacuation of homes and buildings.

Almost all of this billion-dollar annual loss could be prevented. We are doing the right things, but we must do them faster and better.

Perhaps the most preventable loss in the small watershed picture is that of some $88 million a year caused by sediment damage—soil eroded by storms and transported by runoff waters. Sedimentation wantonly shortens the life of our water storage and flood control reservoirs. It increases the cost of maintaining navigation channels. It also causes tremendous harm to our rivers and streams, often making them—over a period of time—almost completely unusable.

Each year more than 380 million cubic yards of sediment —eroded earth—must be dredged out of our harbors and waterways simply to keep them from choking to death. This is more earth than was excavated to build the Panama Canal.

Even though it costs about $125 million a year to dredge out the sediment, this represents only part of the financial loss. Every cubic yard that is dug up was usable elsewhere upstream; it is soil that was torn from its original location by flood waters and then sent careening on its downhill course, causing damage every foot of the way to its ultimate destination.

It has been conservatively estimated that erosion of fertile topsoil on six thousand acres of corn land in the watershed above the supply reservoir of Macomb, Illinois, will create a loss of gross income, in lower yields in that locality, of almost $2 million during the next fifty years. And, of course, the topsoil that is so valuable in those cornfields becomes a costly nuisance in the reservoir into which it flows. This is a single example of a condition that occurs endlessly throughout the country.

There is an innocuous little stream that flows through Washington, D.C., called Rock Creek. It eventually empties into the Potomac about a mile to the north of the Lincoln Memorial. This seemingly harmless creek dumps an average of thirty-four thousand tons of sediment a year into the Potomac. As a matter of fact, the total amount of eroded topsoil deposited into the Anacostia and Potomac Rivers at Washington is estimated to be about 2½ million cubic yards a year. It is hardly astonishing that the silt at the bottom of the Potomac as it oozes past Washington is more than nine feet thick.

Yet, early records of the region show that as long as the original woodlands were permitted to stand along the Potomac, there was very little silt deposited into the river in this area. Because of improper land use, and inadequate protective programs, valuable topsoil that nature required many centuries to form is now being eroded away by a single rainstorm.

Dredging is an unrealistic answer to the problem. For one thing, it is tremendously expensive. Just to keep the open sewer of the Cuyahoga River at Cleveland operating at minimum efficiency costs a million dollars a year in dredging charges. And, of course, such work seeks to cope only with the results; it does not attack the cause, which lies far upstream, in the small watersheds many miles away.

The long-range effects of sedimentation on precious storage space in our reservoirs was too long overlooked. We are becoming increasingly dependent on these reservoirs for hydroelectric power, and for our agricultural, municipal and industrial water supply. This dependency is growing so swiftly that we shall need an estimated *additional 228 million acre-feet* of water storage in reservoirs to meet our ordinary requirements in 1980.

We don't know exactly how much our total reservoir capacity is being robbed by sediment each year, but the most conservative estimates place that loss in the neighborhood of 1½ *billion* cubic yards. If we put the average cost of developing reservoir storage at a hundred dollars per acre-foot (a not excessive estimate), the cost of this largely preventable depreciation comes to $100 million a year.

This, in turn, poses a still thornier problem. All the best sites for our major reservoirs already are being utilized. If these reservoirs continue to fill up with silt until they become useless, we shall have to build new ones. *Where will we build the new dams?*

Consider the situation at Waco, Texas. Lake Waco, on the Bosque River, one of the major water sources for the area, lost half its useful capacity in just seventeen years, because of a buildup of 17,500 acre-feet of sediment. It became necessary to build an expensive new dam to take care of Waco's water problems—just because of siltation.

The pity of it is that most of this could be prevented. But we must attack the problem at the source—in the upstream watersheds, where 70 per cent of the sediment damage occurs and an even higher percentage of the flood damage.

The problem is urgent. The next fifteen years could be decisive. Our population is growing at an accelerating pace and our rate of urban expansion is approaching fantastic proportions. The cost of construction is growing with each passing year.

We should attack the upstream watershed problem boldly and with vision now, before it is too late. If we do this, we shall be able to preserve enough water to keep many areas of the country secure from drought, and we shall be able to save billions of dollars in unnecessary waste throughout the country.

What in the world are we waiting for?

8 From the Seas

"A weary waste of waters!"
  —Southey: *"Madoc in Wales"*

"And to our age's drowsy blood
Still shouts the inspiring sea!"
  —James Russell Lowell: *"Vision of Sir Launfal"*

In the autumn of 1962, Fidel Castro had an idea which he fondly thought to be a stroke of genius.

Ever since he had assumed power as the Communist dictator of Cuba, Castro had inveighed against the occupancy of the Guantánamo Naval Base by the United States Navy. He wanted very badly to kick us off his island. We, on the other hand, refused to be evicted since our rights to the base were secured by a completely valid and irrevocable treaty.

His stroke of genius was to shut off Guantánamo's water supply.

The Navy was buying water from the Cuban government. The Cuban government, merely by turning off a master spigot, could cut off that water. Nobody, of course, could survive without water. Ergo, the militaristic American "imperialists" would have to slink off the island, their tails between their legs, vanquished by Fidel's bold strategem.

185

When Castro turned off the water, the reaction in the United States was fierce and indignant. Senator Barry Goldwater of Arizona spoke for a good many people when he allowed that, if he were President, he would send in a detachment of Marines and turn the water back on, just like that.

President Lyndon B. Johnson was in office only a few months when the crisis occurred. He acted with great wisdom and restraint. First, to solve the immediate problem, he ordered a group of Navy ships to initiate a ferry system between Florida and Guantánamo, carrying fresh water in their holds. Then, he ordered to Guantánamo a very special type of naval vessel, a conversion ship capable of turning hundreds of thousands of gallons of salt water into fresh water, daily.

This somewhat surprising development was obviously only an expedient. The volume of water which the conversion ship made available was not nearly enough to satisfy all the needs of the huge base. The water was expensive, too, costing about four dollars per thousand gallons to produce. And, of course, a ship riding at anchor did not present to the world the image of permanency which we wanted to project.

The third step which President Johnson ordered turned Castro's "stroke of genius" into a fiasco. He directed the Secretary of the Interior to turn over to the Navy the entire Saline Water Conversion Plant at San Diego, California. This demonstration facility had been quietly and efficiently converting a million gallons of salt water a day at a cost of between ninety-five cents and a dollar per thousand gallons.

The plant was swiftly dismantled, shipped through the Panama Canal to Guantánamo and reconstructed. By July

1964, the plant was in full operation. Since that time two auxiliary desalination plants have been built and Guantánamo's water problems have been ended. The last laugh was at the expense of the bearded Cuban who, it turned out, had cut off his own nose to spite his face.

President Johnson's bold solution to this problem has produced many salutary effects. It proved to the world that the United States had a strong President capable of resolute action in a time of crisis. It also deepened the respect of the rest of the world for this nation's technological capability at a time when our reputation needed some polishing. It captured the public imagination in those substantial areas of the world where water is scarce. And, of course, it made millions of Americans aware of the potential of desalination for the first time.

Up until the Guantánamo episode, the average American was inclined to think of this process as a gimmick. Those who served in the air forces in World War II were familiar with a small plastic device in their survival kits which, through a slow process of vaporization, could provide a little fresh water from the sea if one were adrift in a life raft. The idea of transforming this clever little device into a huge operation capable of serving the needs of a large city was considered too remote for serious consideration.

But farsighted men in Congress had been considering the idea ever since the end of the war. In 1950, President Harry S. Truman threw the weight of his office behind the desalination concept when, in his budget message, he said:

Experience in recent years has been that it may not be possible to meet the shortages of water, which are a threat in some areas, through our extensive water-resource programs. I recommend, therefore, that the Congress enact legislation authorizing the initiation of research to find the means for transforming salt water into fresh water in large volume at economical costs.

This statement gave renewed impetus to the efforts of various members of Congress toward this end. In 1952, the late Senator Clair Engle of California, then a Representative, introduced a bill which later became law, authorizing the expenditure of a modest $2 million a year for five years to study the feasibility of converting salt water into usable fresh water.

The program did not prosper during the Eisenhower Administration, which emasculated various budget proposals made along this line by its predecessor. In exasperation during the middle years of Mr. Eisenhower's term of office, a disgruntled conservationist (and, obviously, a Democrat) said: "The President wasn't aware there was a water problem in the United States until the other day when he found the fairways at Burning Tree had turned brown."

This was obviously a partisan exaggeration, both unkind and unfair, but the fact remains that water conservation and, particularly, the desalination program, got little more than lip service from the Executive Branch during the middle 1950's. It took the able and thoughtful Congressman from Alabama, Bob Jones, Chairman of the Government Operations Subcommittee on Public Works and Resources, to reawaken public interest in the problem of finding new sources of water to meet the mushrooming needs of the nation.

During hearings held in 1958, Jones uncovered an appalling indifference to the subject in the executive leadership of the Interior Department and particularly in the Department's

Office of Saline Water. Research and development were proceeding at a slow waltz tempo despite the enthusiasm of the Departmental scientists to get on with the job. During the first five years of the Eisenhower Administration, the desalination program had been granted actual appropriations totaling only $2,125,000—or just a little more in five years than the *annual* authorization permitted under the original legislation.

Bob Jones's Subcommittee produced a withering report which charged the entire Executive Branch with deliberate foot-dragging in this activity. There was an almost complete lack of coordination and cooperation among agencies, it said. Basic research was practically nonexistent. The Office of Saline Water was so understaffed it couldn't undertake even a small part of the task it was designed to perform. So slight was the sense of urgency that the Saline Water Advisory Board, consisting of nine outstanding authorities in the field, named to assist the Secretary of the Interior in implementing the will of the Congress, had met only twice in six years.

The Jones Subcommittee hearings lit a fuse under the Executive Branch and spurred the Congress into renewed aggressive action. Senator Clinton P. Anderson of New Mexico sponsored very useful legislation which directed the construction of five water conversion plants. His bill took the entire program out of the back rooms of theoretical research and put it to work.

When John F. Kennedy became President in 1961, only one of these plants had been started and funds had been appropriated for the construction of just one other. His interest in the program can be judged by the fact that, at the time of his assassination in 1963, when the eastern part of the nation was just beginning to suffer its serious drought, he had the satisfaction of seeing all five plants constructed and of signing into law a bill that will carry the program through 1970 at least, guaranteeing funds not only for these experimental plants but also for accelerated research.

In signing the bill, the Chief Executive said:

I may or may not be the most optimistic person in America about the progress we can make on desalting the seas, but I am, and I intend to remain, the most determined man that we shall make the great breakthrough before the calendar turns in 1970.

President Johnson, in subsequent Executive Orders expediting this work, has declared that our goal is to establish plants before 1968 which will be capable of producing up to ten million gallons of desalted water a day and to make them available to communities that need them. He also has predicted a successful and greatly expanded program of "mining" brackish underground waters throughout the nation. The 1970 target, he has said, is to achieve an output of 100 million gallons of desalinated water daily.

The problem of desalination actually seems less formidable than it is. Sea water, typically, is only 3½ per cent salt. But the human body can distill and get rid of only a 2 per cent salt solution. If the concentration ingested is higher, dehydration occurs as the system tries to rid itself of the excess.

Men have been working toward a practical method of desalination for centuries. The Elizabethans experimented in the field. On November 21, 1791, the Secretary of State of the United States of America, Thomas Jefferson, submitted a report to the Congress urging greater effort in developing

190

techniques and announcing that our ships were already capable of rendering salt water potable in very limited quantities.

Of course, the only practicable application of such techniques at that time would involve our ships at sea. The water supply of the continent far outstripped the demand, and land was so plentiful that it was easy to locate one's home and one's business in an area where the supply was pure, readily accessible and almost inexhaustible. There was no apparent need to develop techniques and pursue research in the field of desalination until the growth of our population, industrialization of society and wasteful use of our resources combined to transform our fresh-water surplus into a serious shortage.

It was not until after President Truman's budget message of 1950, and Clair Engle's bill of 1952, that any significant advances in desalination processes were made. We have come a long way in the intervening years. We have a very long way still to go.

Of course, the potential is unlimited. More than three-fifths of the earth's surface is covered by salt water. It is obvious that, if any major part of this could be made available to man in a fresh state, we never again would want for water.

At present, five techniques of desalination are being tested and used. These techniques have been chosen out of seventeen different workable theories which grew from the preliminary research.

Of the five plants erected, the first to go into operation was that in my home state of Texas, in Freeport, in 1961. It now produces a million gallons a day. The second plant, in San Diego (and now Guantánamo Bay), was activated in 1962 and the third, a few weeks later, at Webster, South Dakota.

191

A fourth was opened at Wrightsville Beach, North Carolina, in January 1963. The fifth and latest was dedicated in July 1963, at Roswell, New Mexico. The total production of all five plants comes to 3½ million gallons a day. This is a small start, but a very promising one.

In his annual report to the President, Secretary of the Interior Stewart L. Udall said that 1964 was the turning point in the desalination program. In that year the emphasis in his Department shifted from technological research to engineering, in order to develop the specific processes chosen for the program to the point of maximum efficiency. He said that the target of producing fresh water below a dollar per thousand gallons was assured and that the immediate goal now was fifty cents per thousand gallons. He expressed doubt that any major, new, dramatic breakthrough could be expected now (although one would be welcomed), and said that the ultimate targets probably would be met through steady and orderly development of the existing processes.

Several communities in the United States have put in their own small plants and are now enjoying truly fresh water for the first time in years. Buckeye, Arizona, was the first U.S. town to pioneer in this field, and its plant now makes potable water out of a brackish supply. Port Mansfield, Texas, followed suit. The water for this town had been so foul that residents drank only bottled water. Now they have enough fresh water for their needs. Avalon, California, located on waterless Catalina Island, off the coast of the southern part of the state, is the third community. Avalon had a special problem, since its year-round population of sixteen hundred rises to more than ten thousand during the summer season.

There are no natural water sources on the island and continued drought had depleted the reservoirs; fresh water had to be transported from the mainland by ship. The South California Edison Company is installing the plant and will also be responsible for supplying electricity and gas to the community.

These three examples are both hopeful and interesting, but they are too few to be really meaningful. More than a thousand cities in the United States report that their water contains at least as much as 1 per cent salt. These communities can, for an initial outlay of about $200,000, acquire their own plants which will supply 250,000 gallons of fresh water a day. The expense would seem well worth it, considering not only the improvement in the quality of the water, but also the elimination of costly damage to pipes and equipment caused by salty and heavily mineralized water.

The Port Mansfield plant, officially dedicated on December 12, 1965, cost a total of $827,000. The water, heavy with salt intrusion from the nearby Gulf of Mexico, is supplied by an artesian well with a capacity of 350 gallons per minute. An 18-mile-long transmission line pipes it over the salt flats to a 100,000-gallon storage tank at Port Mansfield. There the wet stuff is pumped through an electrodialyses process which removes the harmful salt and mineral particles, resulting in pure, potable water. People in this hot southernmost tip of Texas—where citrus growers annually gamble in the millions on the odds against an improbable freeze—are convinced that the desalination plant is just about the best investment they've ever made.

Much hopeful comment has arisen about the potential

value of desalination for the world's underdeveloped countries. For most of these countries, however, the practical application of desalting techniques remains beyond the horizon of present possibilities. The costs are prohibitive. By way of example, a recent survey team of United Nations experts developed the fact that in Madras State in India the use of a thousand gallons of water for rice cultivation yields a gross agricultural income of only .25 rupees, or just about five cents —approximately one-twentieth the cost of removing the salt by present processes.

Admittedly, in arid and semi-arid countries the lack of water has been for many generations the single most formidable barrier against industrial development. But the problem is that in most of these water-short areas the governments have been forced to place primary emphasis upon supplying enough for rudimentary agricultural needs in order to produce sufficient food for their people. And water for basic agricultural uses simply *has* to be *cheap* water. At this stage, it is idle to expect desalination to become inexpensive enough in the foreseeable future to provide water for the cultivation of staple crops.

Moreover, the initial investment required for a desalination plant is, by local standards, quite large. It is justifiable only where there is a concentration of immediate or potential users. In most of the arid underdeveloped lands, alas, the population is small and widely dispersed. It's a vicious cycle.

Some developing countries, however, have attained a state at which desalting has become not only feasible but imperative. Israel is a prime example. Since its founding as a nation in 1948, the Israeli population has almost tripled—from

915,000 to more than 2.6 million in 1965. Three-fourths of this is concentrated, together with the largest towns, along the Mediterranean coastal plain. The principal industries, as well as the citrus plantations, are located there. Citrus—unlike wheat or rice—is a high-yield but salt-sensitive crop. It is Israel's primary agricultural export.

And Israel is rapidly running out of usable water, in spite of a vigorous water-distribution program. This very fact threatens to stymie the country's otherwise promising development. The total fresh-water resources of the nation, according to a report given by Israeli representatives to the first International Symposium on Water Desalination meeting in Washington in October of 1965, are only some 330 billion gallons per year. (About 55 per cent of this is groundwater drawn from wells and springs; approximately 31 per cent comes through the flow of the Jordan River; 5 per cent is trapped from intermittent floods; and 9 per cent represents reclaimed sewage effluent.)

All of these available resources will be fully developed, say the Israelis, by "the early 'seventies." Yet during the year 1964, the nation's total usage already had reached 85 per cent of the maximum developable fresh-water quantity.

The need has been met, in fact, only by temporarily overpumping from a depleting underground supply in the coastal area. And this in turn has been aggravating the problem of excessive salinity to which a number of saline springs along the shores of Lake Tiberias also contribute. Unless something is done, it is estimated that by 1975 the mineral content in the nation's elaborately interconnected water grid will be almost twice the amount which the citrus groves will tolerate.

Faced with this prospect, the Government of Israel in 1959 appointed a Sea Water Conversion Commission to map plans for desalination projects. The Commission advised the government to erect a dual-purpose plant at Eilat on the Red Sea. In addition to serving the needs of the town, it would serve as a demonstration unit for future larger-scale water conversions.

The method finally hit upon at Eilat is a process called "Vacuum Freezing Vapor Compression." Pure ice crystals are produced in brine, simultaneously with the flash evaporation of part of this brine. The ice crystals are then separated from the briny solution and washed, then acted upon by compressed vapor. In a reverse exchange of heat, the vapor condenses, melting the ice which at this point becomes pure water.

The cost comes to just a little over $1 per thousand gallons of fresh water produced, comparing favorably with the other techniques earlier discussed. Israel is pleased with the progress and certain that the investment is worthwhile. The government is engaged now, in fact, in a joint study with the United States pointing to a much larger project which will combine the conversion of salt water with the production of electric power.

All in all, by the end of 1965, a total of more than 125 separate demineralization plants of various types and sizes have been erected. As stated earlier, however, the world's total volume of converted salt water is still infinitesimal when compared with the need.

There is one venture in the desalination program which is really eye-popping and which may turn out to be more valu-

196

able than all the others. The engineers involved feel that this project can be in full operation by 1970. It involves the imaginative use of nuclear power.

In 1964 a three-way agreement was entered into among the Department of the Interior, the Atomic Energy Commission and the Metropolitan Water District of Southern California, calling for the study of the possibilities of constructing a desalination plant in an area in which more than nine million citizens must be served. The studies were completed in February of 1966, and the plant that will eventually evolve should be able to produce between 50 and 150 million gallons a day. (The importance of this can be judged if you remember that the current conversion capacity throughout the entire world is only 50 million gallons a day. The largest single unit in the world, which is on the Caribbean island of Aruba, produces only 3.5 million gallons daily.)

If the advocates of this visionary scheme turn out to be right, water will be produced for about thirty-one cents per thousand gallons. A nuclear power plant also would produce high-pressure steam to generate between 150,000 and 750,000 kilowatt hours of electricity, the sale of which would reduce the cost of desalting the water. The hopefulness of the Atomic Energy Commission can be seen in the fact that it has announced plans to spend $22 million a year for the next ten years on the developing of a practical nuclear desalting process.

Scientists and politicians have been talking hopefully for a long time about the possibility of turning the secrets of nuclear power from destructive uses to constructive ones. The development of desalination processes with the long-range

197

potential of curing the world's water ills, certainly could be one of the greatest beneficial uses to which this awesome power can be put.

It also is worthy of consideration that the development of practical desalination processes could contribute greatly to the cause of world peace. Many of the armed conflicts and recurrent crises in the Near East throughout recorded time involved water, which, in most places, is at a bare subsistence level of supply. The Jordan River, for example, today forms the center of a major controversy involving Israel and the Arab nations. While an efficient desalination program would not subdue all the ancient animosities existing in this area, it would make the controversy over the waters of the Jordan meaningless. (Meanwhile, happy, hot little Kuwait, which awoke one day to find it possesses the richest oil deposits in the world, has its own very effective desalination plant which relieves it of dependency on any other country for its water supply. Things are going so well and so richly in Kuwait that they are now almost seriously considering putting a dome-roof over the entire country and using the desalted water to air-condition the place!)

President Johnson has said that water should never be a cause for war, but a cause for peace. In keeping with this philosophy, the United States is now supporting and assisting Israel in its search for an answer to the water problem.

Significantly, the desalination of water is one area in which the Soviet Union and the United States are freely exchanging scientific data and records. Pragmatic Russia knows she is behind in this field, and also knows the stakes involved.

This is perhaps hopeful thinking, but it just could be that

198

the mutual desire to find an answer to the world's water problems could be a focal point around which a meaningful program of peaceful cooperation between the two divided parts of the world could be built. After all, the water problem is universal. If the solution turns out to be universal, too, who knows what permanent good may derive from it?

9 Oceans Above Us

"I am the daughter of Earth and Water,
  And the nursling of the Sky;
I pass through the pores of the ocean and shores;
  I change, but I cannot die."
  —Shelley: *"The Cloud"*

The 1965 drought in New York, although the most severe in the city's history, is really only one in a series that has extended for many years.

In 1950, when a similar drought afflicted the region, New York's city fathers decided to try to do something about it. They hired a rainmaker.

For years newspapers and other publications had been carrying hopeful and somewhat sensationalized reports of a new technique for creating rain. It consisted of "seeding" cumulus cloud formations either with solid carbon dioxide (dry ice), or with silver iodide pellets. The theory was that these elements, shot into the clouds, would cause ice crystals to form. As these crystals grew heavier, they would fall from the clouds, melting en route, and reach the ground as rain.

Varying degrees of success were reported in different parts of the country. Opinions of qualified observers as to the efficacy of these experiments also varied. Some said flatly that rain could be induced, if not created, if the right techniques were used on the right kinds of clouds. Others scoffed at the whole idea, attributing the "success" of such experiments to coincidence, claiming that the rains would have come anyway, whether men had tampered with the clouds or not.

The rainmaker whom New York City engaged called himself a "weather modification expert." He set a fee of a hundred dollars a day, plus expenses. His proposition accepted, he made plans to seed the clouds.

Naturally, to impregnate the clouds merely over the city itself would produce only minimally beneficial results. Rain falling upon New York City would be of little use to anyone, since most of it would run off the streets into the storm sewers and would lose itself in the Hudson River and, eventually, the Atlantic Ocean.

The "weather modification expert," quite sensibly, decided to conduct his experiments over the city's upper watershed, in the Catskill Mountains.

By any standards, the experiment must be judged as having been a complete success—for New York City. Immediately after this practitioner concluded his cloud seeding, the rains came. And they came. They continued for days on end in an almost constant deluge. The city fathers of New York were delighted. The drought was broken. The reservoirs were filled to the brim. The expert's bill was paid, cash on the barrelhead.

Oddly enough, the expert himself proved to be excessively modest about his accomplishments. He publicly disclaimed any credit for having induced the deluge and gave it as his official opinion that the rains probably would have fallen anyway whether he had been hired or not.

If this seems a curious attitude on the part of a pioneer who had just made such a conspicuous ten-strike in his particular field of endeavor, it should be remembered that the Catskill Mountains are an extremely popular summer resort area. The deluge, whether artificially induced or not, drowned the resorts for almost two weeks, ruined thousands of vacations and reduced the innkeepers' income, in the heart of the season, to a mere shadow of its accustomed size. The angry resort owners immediately filed suits for damages amounting to more than $1.5 million. It is no wonder that neither the weather modification expert nor any official spokeman for New York City was eager to claim the credit for having brought about a scientific triumph.

And, indeed, it would be absurd to make any scientific claims because of the apparent success of a single experiment.

By way of contrast, in the middle of the 1965 summer drought, I attended the annual picnic of the Texas State Society, a social organization of Texans living and working in the District of Columbia area. The day was hot and sunny with not even the vaguest hint of cloud visible anywhere on the horizon. The Weather Bureau had predicted no break in the dry spell.

As part of the day's entertainment, a troupe of American Indians performed a series of dances, including a particularly colorful one designed by the ancients to induce rain. Almost as if by magic, a breeze started up at the conclusion of their dance and clouds began to make their appearance in the distance. Within two hours the picnic was washed out by a good half-inch of rain—the first precipitation the area had experienced in several weeks. (As one of the drenched guests remarked: "Okay, so those Indians danced for some rain, but this is *ridiculous!*")

The truth is that man will try almost anything to coax enough rain at the right time out of the skies. The desperate quest for water has not only brought forth serious experimenters like the weather modification expert who may (or may not) have caused the deluge in the Catskills, but it also has produced whole armies of charlatans and fakes who have bilked their sponsors and thrown discredit upon the entire idea of artificially induced precipitation. It would not have surprised me in the least if some communities had engaged a troupe of Indian rain dancers during the summer of 1965 in the serious hope that it might possibly work.

The clouds above us do form an enormous potential reservoir which is only partially tapped. It seems inconceivable, but even the most violent kind of cloudburst removes only about 15 per cent, at the very maximum, of the water available in the overhead clouds. Rarely, in fact, does the attrition of a given rain ever rise above 5 per cent of the water burden in the cloud formation. The rest of the moisture is wafted away and dissipated elsewhere, returning to the oceans. Imagine what we could accomplish if we could tap this huge, floating reservoir at will, inducing rain to fall, when and where it is needed. Deserts would blossom, our lakes could be permanently full, man might be forever free from the fear of drought. The possibilities are limitless.

Man has been seeking ways to tap these overhead oceans since the beginning of recorded time. Primitive man prayed

203

to the rain gods. In the early part of this century, attempts were made to create rain by firing cannon into cloudbanks. Later, some daring aviators tried to get results by dropping bombs with time fuses set to explode among the cumuli. Nothing worked—at least not with any predictable precision.

Perhaps the first serious scientific attempt to create rain artificially occurred in 1946 when researchers from the General Electric laboratories in Schenectady, New York, used an airplane to seed some clouds with dry ice. Observers noted a trace of rain following the experiment, but refused to claim positively that the precipitation was its direct result.

Since that time, the federal government has spent an estimated $12 million on tens of thousands of similar experiments throughout the country. Many more millions have been spent on commercial efforts to bring rain down on water-starved clients. Many other nations have joined in the quest for a foolproof solution to the problem.

Unfortunately, the progress of the serious experimenters has been retarded by the enthusiasm of overeager laymen. Uncontrolled attempts at cloud seeding have resulted in overestimates of success and in patently false claims. Professional phonies have exploited the desires of optimistic farmers and others and turned the rainmaking business into a kind of aerial confidence game. These pseudoscientific charades have dimmed public confidence and made government support of the artificial rain inducement program subject to ridicule and thus difficult to achieve.

It may be that the charlatan fringe has caused the serious scientists to be even more conservative than they usually are. Scientists, of course, prefer to experiment in relative privacy and make announcements of success only when such success can be proved beyond any conceivable doubt. Even today, it is next to impossible to find a reputable scientist engaged in this field who will make the flat assertion that it is possible for man to cause the rain to fall.

Nonetheless, the fact that the scientists are working constantly to solve the problem is proof that a high degree of guarded optimism exists. And certain recent programs indicate, at least to an informed layman, that there is hope of at least a partial breakthrough in this area.

One such program involved an eight-year series of experiments conducted by the University of Arizona over the Santa Catalina Mountains near Tucson. Airplanes were used to seed cloud formations upwind from the mountain range. The seedings were scrupulously controlled and documented; they were timed, recorded by cloud photography, by radar recordings and by visual observation. Rain gauges recorded precipitation throughout the entire eight-year history of the project.

After the first two years of the program, the scientists made a very cautious report of their findings. Among other things, it said:

When data from both years were combined, it was found that the mean rainfall per gauge was 30 percent higher on the seeded days.

Now that, to the average layman, would indicate a very satisfactory state of affairs. But wait. The next sentence adds a note of caution:

However, the probability that the observed differences in the mean rainfall occurred by chance was quite high, about 0.14.

Later on, we find another line that strikes a note of hope:

A comparison of the extreme rainfalls on seeded and nonseeded days showed a great difference.

But immediately the scientists add a stern disclaimer:

The statistical confidence of a real difference was not sufficiently high to be acceptable.

In conclusion, the report exhibits a very reserved confidence:

Although the results to date point toward the conclusion that seeding produced important effects, it is vital that more data be compiled in order to be sure that the results have not been brought about by chance.

In short, the report *seems* to say: We think there may be something to this rainmaking business, but we can't really prove it, and for heaven's sake, don't quote us.

I don't want to seem critical of the cautious scientific approach to the evalution of observed data. I admire the insistence upon absolute proof before making a positive assertion. It is a kind of meticulousness that is not often encountered in the political arena in which I work, and I find it refreshing —if a little frustrating.

I might add that with the eight-year series of tests now concluded, the scientists still are so cautious that they have issued an evaluation covering only the first four of those years. The report, while admitting that a vast amount of data has been collected, analyzed and correlated, concludes that a program of *fifty years* should be conducted "before the question of whether or not man can induce rainfall can be answered yes or no!"

This recommendation is made in spite of the fact that the

tests show a 30 per cent increase in rainfall factor during seeding operations versus nonseeding periods.

I dislike exhibiting a typical layman's impatience, but if there really is something to it, we should not be compelled to wait another half century to determine whether or not we can milk the clouds of their moisture at will. We need the water, and we need it very soon. We must make up our minds whether to continue and intensify our present seeding techniques, or to abandon them in favor of other approaches. We cannot afford indefinitely to let the clouds scud over us untapped, while our cities and farms dry up due to unnecessary aridity—if indeed there *is* something we can do about it.

The Arizona tests do seem to indicate that the incidence of success in rain inducement is greater over mountainous areas than over flat lands. This is hopeful for the mountainous, western part of the United States which needs the rainfall if it is to survive. Since 65 per cent of our land area receives only 25 per cent of our rainfall, the desirability of distributing the nation's rain more evenly is apparent. If sufficient controlled rainfall can be created over the Rocky Mountain watersheds, massive reservoirs could be built in that area. They would be a constant source of water, an inducement for useful industrial decentralization and a solution to many of our problems.

While the airplane is the most often used device for impregnating the clouds, other forms of intrusion have been tried, with varying degrees of success. Rockets and free-flying balloons have been used. These, however, are not as accurate in their seeding as is the aircraft. Besides, in this experimental stage, the airplane affords a better opportunity

207

to photograph and make radar recordings of the effects of the seeding.

The most common method used seems also to be the least effective—that of projecting crystals into the clouds from ground-based generators. Since these generators must be relatively near the target area, they usually are located on mountain tops where visual factors are limited, where changing wind currents disrupt the seeding plans, and where the seeding agents are inclined to evaporate too swiftly on their way to the clouds. So far, it has not been possible to subject ground-based operations to sufficient scientific controls, so the experts have been unable to draw even a reasonable amount of solid conclusion from the experiments.

As an example, experts on one project were greatly elated when their attempt to induce rainfall through ground generators was followed by a torrential downpour. Subsequent investigation found that their apparatus had not been in working order and not one crystal had been discharged into the clouds.

Because the results are so uncertain and so difficult of documentation, this technique has not been sanctioned for federally financed studies.

Official studies to establish whether or not we can induce rainfall seldom make the headlines. Their reports of success or failure are not published piecemeal, but are merely added to the large and growing body of scientific data on the subject.

When a commercial operator goes into an area to try to induce precipitation, he makes news whether he apparently succeeds, or whether he fails. If rainfall does occur, he is hailed as a miracle worker. If it does not occur, the doubters and scoffers have a field day with him.

However, it is the quiet experimentation, financed by the federal government and by private institutions, which must form the basis for our hopes.

An enormous amount of information is being developed by these highly constrolled experiments. Already there is a wealth of data available, and much of it is hopeful. But until the scientists are willing to state unequivocally that yes, it is possible to create rainfall when and where we want it, their programs will not gain any great degree of public acceptance and will remain in the realm of pure research.

It is prayerfully to be hoped that someday soon the scientific community will feel sufficiently confident to urge the government and private enterprise to go all out in the development of a proven rain creation program. One-quarter of our population at least faces the real danger of water starvation unless they can learn to make effective use of the oceans of water passing over their land.

Certainly, the results to date indicate that the government should continue to finance these programs until the riddle is solved, one way or another.

As a lay observer, but also as one who has studied many of the reports on past projects, I must say that I find it impossible to believe that man's ingenuity will not find a way to tap the clouds so as to bring the benefits of rain to those who need it so desperately.

We shall find the answer. Let us hope that it will not be too late.

I can report, also, that most of the old-timers in the weather modification field—even though they desire to remain anonymous at this time—share my optimism. However, they feel that if the program is to succeed, it must receive more adequate financing, more adequate staff personnel and more and better equipment. Both the U.S. Weather Bureau and the National Science Foundation remain strong advocates of continuing this vital research as vigorously as we know how.

But all the scientists with whom I talked were unanimous in their belief that the federal government must develop a much greater sense of urgency in this area, and make it a major program rather than a minor one. Both the Executive and the Legislative branches of the government must learn to act with more boldness and more conviction.

And, why shouldn't they? The need for success is urgent; the benefits to be derived are boundless.

I have mentioned the Legislative and Executive branches of government. The Judiciary also is involved.

As one eminent scientist, who shall be nameless, told me: "I, for one, would be reluctant to commit research dollars for experiments until I had assurance that they could be carried to completion without legal entanglements inherent to the program."

The legal questions are thorny. Who owns the clouds? Are we entitled to take all the moisture we want from the clouds passing overhead and, perhaps, deprive our neighbors downwind of their fair share of the rain? Is there a sort of vertical riparian right? If a farmer needs rain for his crops and a resort owner needs dry weather for his vacationing guests, who decides what the weather shall be? Who should get preferential treatment?

As an illustration of some of the complexities that can ensue, a group of fruit growers in West Virginia recently hired a commercial weather-modification company to seed clouds in order to suppress the hail that was tearing up their crops. In the eyes of the fruit farmers, the project was a complete success. No hail fell. But drought-stricken dairymen to their east in adjoining Maryland had other ideas. Since the normal flow of cloud cover in the United States is from west to east, the Maryland dairymen contended that the West Virginians were milking the clouds dry before they crossed the border, leaving no possibility of rain for their pastures.

The argument became heated and acrimonious. It was taken up by the legislatures of both states. The Maryland Legislature finally passed a bill which declared a moratorium on cloud seeding for at least two years. Although this legislation had no force in West Virginia, it—along with threats of injunctions and litigation in the federal courts—caused a temporary suspension of seeding operations in that state.

There have been many similar controversies throughout the country. In some cases, communities charged their neighbors with theft of water which should have fallen on their land. In other cases, the communities blamed rainmaking attempts elsewhere for floods and water damage.

It does not take a lawyer to see that the legal complications involved could hold back the weather modification program for twenty years, even if it received the complete approval of the scientific community.

Who has the authority for conducting the rainmaking experiments? Who has the responsibility for monitoring the expenditures and deciding which aspects of the program should be continued, which expanded and which eliminated?

Under an Act of Congress, dated July 11, 1958, the authority to initiate and support basic research was lodged with the

National Science Foundation. The law directs the Foundation to give particular attention "to areas that have experienced floods, drought, hail, lightning, fog, tornadoes or other weather phenomena." This is a pretty broad mandate, to say the least. (This is especially true of the phrase *"other weather phenomena,"* which can be interpreted to mean everywhere and anywhere within our national boundaries.)

The Foundation can, and does, consult with meteorologists and other scientists in and out of government. It makes grants, and enters into contracts with research institutes, public and private. It may accept gifts of money, material and other services from private and public sources. It can borrow personnel and property from other agencies of government.

A very important provision of the law permits the Foundation to hold hearings and gather information, with the power of subpoena. It also permits the organization to inspect books, records and writings, as well as premises and property.

The Foundation has not nearly the staff or facilities to conduct such research, nor to carry out all the programs in which it is authorized to engage, but it has the backing of the law to do so when and as it is possible.

This pretty well covers the federal area of law. But, what about the states? Here we find confusion, contradictions and a plethora of negative thinking.

Twenty-five of our states have laws concerning weather modification. No single pattern is followed. Some of the state laws claim the right to all the water in all the clouds that pass over their boundaries. Other laws permit state agencies, universities and local authorities to conduct weather modification experiments of their own. Most of the laws attempt to restrict and restrain the activities of private organizations in this field. (The Maryland law, mentioned earlier, is the most sweeping and the harshest of these.)

Many of the statutes are highly restrictive in nature, controlling the conditions under which experiments can be conducted and the conditions under which modification equipment can be manufactured, sold, leased or even advertised. Others establish minimum technical qualifications for cloud seeders and require that they prove the financial ability to withstand the cost of any harm they might do. Still others require licensing, advance notice of seeding operations and the filing of reports after the operations have been completed.

The majority of state laws covering this field contain a mixture of these elements. Although the laws, for the most part, are well intentioned, they do constitute, *en masse*, a legal jungle that could keep a generation of lawyers fat with fees.

Certainly, under present conditions, as the interest in rain-making increases, we can expect a mounting increase in the number of claims against the government. Wherever tests are conducted, the government is going to be blamed for whatever weather phenomena occur within miles of the testing site. (For corroboration of this opinion, I suggest consideration of the fantastic number of claims against the Air Force for alleged damage caused by sonic booms.)

And, to present the other side of the coin, while the experts do not believe they will ever be able, even by accident, to create catastrophic conditions, they admit that, at this experimental stage, their knowledge is too limited to rule out such a possibility entirely.

As of now, there are no court decisions covering federal

liabilities under such a program. Contractors and others working under federal grants are acutely aware of the state laws and, consequently, are uneasy about what could happen to them in court if they lack the protection of the federal law. Even officers of the government have expressed wariness as to just what could happen to them while the present legal vacuum is permitted to exist.

Only one existing statute—the Federal Tort Claims Act—can be currently invoked for recovery of damages caused by officers and employees of the U.S. government. But this act is couched in such carefully circumscribed language that many legal experts doubt that it could be applied in a rainmaking case.

Despite what the law can or cannot do, there is a moral responsibility to provide adequate protection for people and property in case of accident or miscalculation. If we make certain that this responsibility is met, we can continue our experimentation in a far more healthy legal and scientific climate.

However, legalistic considerations aside, I am absolutely convinced that the federal government must conduct a greatly stepped-up and expanded weather modification program which should include every phase of the activities we have discussed.

State and local efforts, and those of private organizations, universities and institutions, should be coordinated and incorporated into one massive program, with central facilities for the free exchange of information and data. This would not only bring greater efficiency, it would reduce wasteful overlapping and duplication to a minimum.

214

Further than that, I believe this program should be considered on an emergency basis. I feel we are so close to success that a major effort could produce a major breakthrough, and this might be a substantial part of our answer to the total water crisis.

It may be that this program will take so long before completion that we shall not ourselves be the immediate beneficiaries of our efforts and of our expenditure of money. But, certainly, our children and our children's children will inherit from us a land greatly enriched by our foresight and sacrifice.

Considering how much our generation has done to denude and despoil the land that we inherited, this seems to be the least we can do.

10 From the Distance: The New Dimension

"Where there is no vision, the people perish."
—Proverbs XXIX:18

"Imagination rules the world."
—Napoleon

In previous chapters we have discussed various means of heading off the coming water famine in the United States. These include the very necessary expedients of cleaning up our streams and freeing them from deadly pollution, the building of small dams and other conservation and flood-prevention devices up in the mountains and hills among the subsidiary streams, an extra head of steam behind the desalination of water from the seas, and the possible uses of weather-modification techniques in order to take advantage of the huge oceans of usable water which float above us, and past us, in the form of clouds.

All these techniques are essential to our future. None is totally adequate. As our per capita use of water increases, and as our demands grow heavier and harder to fulfill, the

216

need will become ever more urgent for a bold plan which will make the demands of tomorrow answerable.

By plain and simple arithmetic, the nation has enough water to supply our total foreseeable needs. But too much of the best water is in the wrong places. Since we can't move all the people to where the water is, obviously we need to move the water to where the people are.

The next logical step is the orderly transportation of water on a growing scale from areas where its overabundance is both a waste and a curse, to areas where it is desperately needed.

Perhaps California has pointed the way. In our most populous state, 70 per cent of the water supply originates in the northern third of the state's geographic area. Conversely, 77 per cent of the water needs lie in the comparatively arid southern two-thirds of the state.

In 1960, the Californians (particularly, the Southern Californians who controlled the majority of the votes) decided in a bond election to spend $1.75 billion to finance the distribution of water from the areas of continuous surplus to the areas of chronic shortage.

The keystone in this sweeping concept is the Oroville Dam on the Feather River, the largest embankment dam in the world, which will tower a staggering 747.5 feet (as high as a sixty-two-story building) above the stream bed. This dam represents the largest civil construction contract ever awarded competitively in the United States ($120.8 million). This and supplementary contracts will bring the cost of construction up to $439 million before the job is completed, in 1968.

The Oroville Dam is the most extensive job of earth-moving ever attempted in the nation's history. It requires the moving of *155 million tons* of material an average of eleven miles to the dam site. It will, incidentally, be a multiple-purpose project with extensive recreational facilities which will be ready as soon as the 3,484,000-acre-foot reservoir is filled.

But the point of the whole operation is the California Aqueduct—a 444-mile conduit which will take the water stored by the Oroville lake into Central and Southern California. Thus, water that otherwise would flow uselessly into the ocean will be pumped through valleys and over mountain ranges to serve the booming communities of Southern California which are already starving for water. The first deliveries from this new fresh-water supply are promised for 1971 and 1972.

By any standard, this is a massive concept demanding the respect and attention of anyone with concern for the water problems of the land. But, great as it is, it is comparatively small change when compared to a program called NAWAPA.

Americans are famous for thinking big. But the NAWAPA idea, first conceived by the late Donald McCord Baker, former water planning engineer for Los Angeles County, adds a new dimension to big thinking in the water field.

NAWAPA means North American Water and Power Alliance. When Baker and the Ralph M. Parsons Company (whom Baker enlisted in support of the idea) brought the proposal before a Senate subcommittee headed by Senator Frank E. Moss of Utah, they caused a sensation among those who heard them out. As one amazed Senator, Frank Church of Idaho, said:

Whether or not this proposal is advanced further, whether or not it is adopted, we must not be deterred by its size. To perform the great task before us may well need a program as farsighted as was the Louisiana Purchase.

The NAWAPA idea consists, first, of building huge dams in Alaska and the Canadian Yukon to trap the abundant water of the various broad rivers in those areas, where the resource is little needed. (The drainage area to be tapped involves 1,300,000 square miles with an annual precipitation which ranges up to sixty inches.)

The program then calls for (hold your hats!) conducting the waters into a largely man-made reservoir *five hundred miles long,* using the natural gorge of the Rocky Mountain Trench. In order to do this, it will be necessary to build a series of connecting tunnels, canals, lakes, dams and even lifts. (En route the water can be sold for the creation of electric power, and then reused.)

At the northern end of the Trench, NAWAPA proposes to dredge a thirty-foot-deep canal all the way to Lake Superior, supplying the Great Lakes with the fresh water they so badly need. Another division of the canal would feed water into the upper stretches of the Mississippi and Missouri Rivers.

A series of dams and power stations would lift the water up to the three-thousand-foot altitude of the Rocky Mountain Trench, a natural geological defile in southwestern British Columbia, from five to fifteen miles wide, which stretches for a length of about nine hundred miles. The site for the big storage reservoir would be the five hundred downstream miles of the southern end of the Trench.

From the Trench Reservoir water would be pump-lifted to the Sawtooth Reservoir in northwestern Montana. From this point, the water would flow southward by gravity, via lined

219

canals and tunnels, throughout the western part of the system, passing the Sawtooth Mountain barrier through a tunnel eighty feet in diameter and fifty miles in length.

This water would help mightily to meet the needs of the western states for irrigation, industry, power, recreation and municipal conservation.

Outflow from the Peace River Reservoir, located at the north end of the Trench Reservoir, would supply the Canadian-Great Lakes-St. Lawrence complex. In excess of 48 million acre-feet of water a year would reach Lake Superior and provide for irrigation and the other water demands of Alberta, Saskatchewan, Manitoba and western Ontario. This important part of the system also could yield considerable hydroelectric power.

The Canadian-Great Lakes Waterway would alleviate falling water levels and pollution in the Great Lakes and, in addition, would augment the power potential of the Niagara and St. Lawrence Rivers.

The NAWAPA concept also includes a seaway between Lake Winnipeg and Hudson Bay. Another seaway would connect Georgian Bay with James Bay. A barge canal would connect the ore fields of Labrador and Quebec with the Great Lakes.

Still other canals would feed existing river systems in Canada, the United States and Mexico.

Thus, the abundant waters of Alaska and Canada would be made available to the parched and unproductive areas of the entire continent. The deserts would become productive. Cities would no longer be hampered and restricted in their growth by a rapidly diminishing water supply.

The Great Lakes would receive an increase of 40 million acre-feet of water each year. This (along with pollution control measures mentioned earlier) would resuscitate the dying Lakes and make them totally useful to mankind once again. The electrical power output of Niagara Falls, for example, would be increased by 50 per cent.

NAWAPA would give an abundance of water to seven provinces of Canada, thirty-three of the United States, and to three northern states of Mexico. In all, 110 million acre-feet of water—all of which is now going to waste—would flow through the system each year. The maximum potential is estimated at 250 million acre-feet—or about 36 *trillion* gallons a year.

The potential electrical power output would be somewhere between an estimated 70 million kilowatts and 150 million kilowatts.

This sounds marvelous. It also sounds expensive. It is both. The program calls for a twenty-year construction cycle costing an estimated $100 billion. However, the proponents of the program claim that the system could be placed in complete operation by 1995 (at the latest) and that it would pay itself off in five decades through the sale of water and power. This is an estimate based on current engineering techniques. It well could be that new techniques (stimulated by the challenge of the program itself) could reduce both the time element and the eventual cost.

This dream is, admittedly, both grandiose and visionary. However, the nation was built by visionaries. There have been some disturbing indications in recent years that we may have lost some of our capacity for dreaming and acting

221

in those areas concerning our survival upon this earth. We must recapture that capability if we are to survive the effects of our own careless profligacy, our wanton wastefulness in the matter of water.

NAWAPA has an almost limitless potential if we possess the courage and the foresight to grasp it. As far as the United States is concerned, the NAWAPA plan would:

Deliver 78 million acre feet of water annually for industrial, municipal and agricultural use;

Make 38 million kilowatts of power available to the northern section of the United States and Alaska;

Provide a north-south seaway connecting Alaska with the northern states of the U.S.;

Increase irrigable land by 40 million acres;

Stabilize and control the level of the Great Lakes by providing more than 40 million acre-feet of clean water annually. (This would save the Lakes from the growing cancer of pollution and would once more permit maximum ship loads in and out of Great Lakes ports);

Provide an access canal through Lake Huron to Hudson Bay;

Increase the annual national income from agriculture, livestock, mining and manufacturing by approximately $30 *billion*.

Mexico also would be a considerable beneficiary of the program.

It would get 20 million acre-feet of water a year for industrial, municipal and agricultural use.

It would increase its irrigable land by 300 per cent.

It would increase its annual income from agricultural, livestock, mining, manufacturing, steel and textile industries by $30 billion.

It would add to its electrical output capacity by 2 million kilowatts, 60 per cent of which would be generated in Mexico.

Canada, of course, would benefit tremendously.

NAWAPA would produce for Canada 22 million acre-feet of water a year for industrial, municipal and agricultural use.

It would provide 30 million kilowatts of power for sale, in addition to the 30 million which the system would purchase itself for pumping purposes.

It would add $2 billion a year from entirely new sources to Canada's annual national income.

It would provide a seaway from the Atlantic Ocean to the heart of Alberta (via the St. Lawrence and the Great Lakes) as well as a network of vital canal routes.

It would stabilize the level of Lake Winnipeg for the protection of existing farmlands and for the recovery of new farmlands. (Of course, the benefits to the Great Lakes listed above would also accrue to Canada.)

It would increase Canada's annual income from agriculture, livestock, mining and manufacturing by approximately $9 billion annually.

There are many obstacles, besides the money, which lie in the way. Canada, for instance, is understandably reluctant to participate financially in the program to the extent that we'd like. After all, the water problem is basically ours, and we have been the profligate ones, wasting and befouling our water supplies as if there were never to be a tomorrow. And most of the waters we'd appropriate are, remember, *Canadian* waters. In the Great Lakes area we have been responsible also for contaminating water which belongs to Canada just as much as it does to us. Many Canadians have yet to be convinced that this program will benefit them sufficiently to justify their participation.

Before NAWAPA can become a reality, an almost inexhaustible number of diplomatic, legal, economic, engineering, social and management problems must be ironed out. Whether or not they *can* be ironed out is still in doubt. Personally, I think the potential benefits are so great—and so greatly needed—that these problems *must* be ironed out.

The fact remains: There is to the north of us a stupendous supply of water, enough to satisfy most of our predictable wants for years to come, which is simply going to waste. We need the water. We need to develop the means of getting that water.

There are many other less romantic illustrations of the increasing need for moving large quantities of water from one place to another. Some of this has been done in our country. Much more of it will need to be done in the future. This is, in fact, the new dimension in water-resources development.

Yet, strangely enough, the idea of transporting water for relatively great distances is not really new at all. In Rome, this was performed by a series of aqueducts which ran for a total of some 250 miles to bring clear water from the Alps to cultivate a flourishing civilization. Some of the structures still may be seen by tourists intent on viewing the antiquities of the Roman Empire days. By means of these farsighted engineering innovations, the Eternal City survived at a time when less audacious Mediterranean cultures were drying up.

The California proposal mentioned in the early part of this chapter is by no means the first such program to be undertaken in that state. Los Angeles and the Imperial Valley have sparked their fantastic boom for a generation by moving water over staggering physical barriers, with tunnels

224

drilled through the mountainsides, from distances of five hundred miles.

Yet the California experience indicates something of the resistance which any such proposals are likely to encounter from those residing in the areas of water abundance whenever it is suggested that *their* water be transported to some other area. This is sometimes true even when the life-giving fluid exists in such abundance that it is a curse rather than a blessing.

In January of 1965, I toured the flood-damaged areas of northern California and Oregon as a member of a Congressional investigating team. Pathos lay in the wake of the raging tide. Entire communities had been washed down the river on the cruel crest of the rampaging streams. Bridges, twisted and crushed like toys in the hands of a giant, made a grotesque mockery of man's puny efforts in face of an outraged nature.

The committee stopped and held hearings at several localities. It was at one of these hearings that I proposed a massive plan to divert quantities of these potential floodwaters at their sources and convey them by pipelines, tunnels or canals to water-thirsty Southern California and Arizona. After the meeting, one lady—whose family had suffered appreciable loss along with others of the community—approached me and indignantly demanded to know: "Where do you get off with that crazy notion of sending *our* water to Southern California?"

Her comment, fortunately, was not typical. Most of those with whom I talked were more than willing to share the com-

225

modity which, in its oversupply, had just wrought havoc with their communities.

In many sections of our land—and particularly in the West and Southwest—cities are learning that the nearest solution to their water shortages lies many miles away.

Denver has a program involving thirty-seven miles of tunnels and fifty-one miles of connecting canals to bring more water to that city. We already have spoken of New York City's reliance upon the distant Catskills.

Oklahoma City is relying for its future growth on the abundant storage reservoirs in southeastern Oklahoma, approximately 125 miles removed. My city of Fort Worth presently pipes water from a reservoir on Richland Creek, more than seventy-five miles away, and has contemplated a plan involving waters from the State of Oklahoma.

Dallas, a few years ago, completed a project to pipe water from the Red River, more than fifty miles to the north, and still did not solve its problem. The Red River water, heavy in brackish solutions, needed more filtration and treatment than the city's system was geared to provide. Meanwhile, other reservoirs have been built, but all of them require water pipelines to bring their beneficence to Dallas.

These are but a few random examples. Multiply this picture by several hundred cities whose phenomenal growth is thrusting upon them the necessity to look around over ever-widening areas for the nearest dependable water supply, and you will have a general idea of the enormity of the problem.

The time has arrived in our water planning when most western communities, and many eastern ones as well, must begin to think seriously not only of impounding water but of transporting it, often over great distances.

226

For most such communities, one staggering barrier looms between them and realization of the goal. This is the hurdle of financing. The unprecedented growth which most cities have encountered in recent years has forced upon them many unusual expenses and required them to assume growing obligations of bonded indebtedness.

Many communities are nearing their debt limitations for municipal bonds, and this has made it more and more difficult for them to finance such costly projects as lengthy pipelines, indispensable though such projects may be to their future. Clearly, the problem of financing is a major bottleneck. The survey to which I referred in an earlier chapter revealed that fully 50 per cent of the most rapidly growing cities are straining against the straitjacket of their bonding capacity.

A few year's ago, I introduced a bill aimed at establishing machinery by which the federal government would be able to aid states, cities and water districts in overcoming the roadblock of financing which lies across the path of their future growth and development. Lyndon B. Johnson, then the senior Senator from our state, introduced a companion measure in the Senate.

This proposal has not been acted upon by Congress, largely because the enormity and near universality of the problem has not yet been fully grasped by lawmakers. Another obstacle, I discovered, lay in the question of which of our existing agencies—the Department of Interior or the Corps of Army Engineers—should administer such an undertaking. Frankly, I don't think it would make a great deal of difference.

Under the terms of the bill I introduced, the Corps of Army Engineers would review each proposal for building water transportation facilities. The Corps would determine, first, whether a given project is feasible; second, whether it will enhance overall water conservation in a river basin; and third, the extent to which it would affect other water uses, including flood control and navigation.

If a proposed development passed these criteria, the government would be authorized to purchase up to one-third of the bonds at the going government interest rate. Assuming $2 million worth of forty-year bonds purchased, the economy in interest alone could result in a saving of approximately $240,000 to the city or water district.

The main advantage, of course, would be to stimulate action by making it possible for local authorities to get on with the job.

In addition, when it is found that such a development would aid flood control by relieving an overabundant area of potential floodwaters, the government would be permitted to participate in the actual cost of the project to the extent of such flood-control benefits derived.

An example would be water taken from the Missouri River, where the recurrent overburden has been for years a menace to downstream inhabitants. For generations it has been proposed that quantities of this water could be channeled to semiarid localities in the Midwest and Southwest where it would be a blessing and a boon to industry, municipal development and agriculture.

It is, perhaps, worthy of note that the late Senator Huey P. Long of Louisiana, in 1935, just a few months before his assassination, published an ambitious little book entitled *My First Days in the White House*. One of his major proposals was a massive engineering program to divert part of the Missouri River through the dry plains of Kansas and Oklahoma. So the need has been long-discussed.

The Long book, abounding with the unquestioning and presumptuous self-confidence of the late Kingfish, was doomed ironically to gain only a limited circulation. Appearing after his assassination, it seemed strangely anticlimatic, perhaps even a bit macabre.

The publishers, The Telegraph Press of Harrisburg, Pa., explained in a modest foreword: "This volume is presented as a prophecy by its Author, the late Huey Pierce Long, wherein he endeavored to portray what he would have done had he become President and how he would have conducted national government. . . ."

With Huey, however, it clearly was never a question of *if*, but of *when*. The manuscript makes it clear that he confidently anticipated his election to the Presidency in 1936—a curious thing, considering the phenomenal but then still-untested popularity of FDR. Huey's Cabinet was to include Roosevelt as Secretary of the Navy, Herbert Hoover as Secretary of Commerce and Al Smith as Director of the Budget.

If Long's style was flamboyant, his methods sometimes crude and his ambition unrestrained, it is true also that he had flashes of vision. One key point in his "program" was to be a massive development and redirection of the great western rivers, a total package of some 1,600 individual projects to serve flood control, navigation, irrigation and dust bowl eradication. The whole undertaking, he figured, would have cost $2 billion a year and taken five years to accomplish, but it would have "increased the wealth of America by not less than some 50 to 100 billions of dollars."

The basic efficacy of this particular plan is seen in the fact that, beginning in 1936 (the year following the book's publication), most of it indeed has been done—although at a much slower pace than that envisioned by the late Kingfish.

We are entering an era in which we must add an entirely new dimension to our water planning. In much of the nation, underground water tables are falling precipitately. No longer can we assure adequate supply simply by erecting dams and impoundments. Increasingly, our water problems will be solved only by moving water from areas of comparative abundance to sections of critical scarcity.

It is a great engineering frontier in which lie vistas of unparalleled opportunity. Two enormously important scientific breakthroughs, the development of cheap power and the economical conversion of salt waters, lie just beyond the horizon.

With the achievement of these goals, the long-distance moving of water will become a common practice. Former Secretary of the Interior Fred Seaton predicted that by 1990 we shall see "a network of pipelines criss-crossing America, carrying fresh and palatable water dredged from the sea."

It is certainly not too early to set up some machinery under which the nation can be meeting its water needs before they become crises and developing the kind of experience which will equip us to cope intelligently with this growing problem of the future.

In wartime the United States has traditionally gathered together all the elements of its national capability and conquered problems of seemingly insuperable magnitude. Under the stimulus of World War II and our huge national appetite for petroleum, we spanned the continent with the Big Inch and Little Inch pipelines. They cost an enormous amount of money. They had the emphasis of emergency. But, if you had your choice, which would you prefer to do without—oil and gas, or water?

The crisis of our diminishing water resources is just as severe (if less obviously immediate) as any wartime crisis we have ever faced. Our survival is just as much at stake as it was at the time of Pearl Harbor, or the Argonne, or Gettysburg, or Saratoga.

We must apply the same fortitude, the same bold and imaginative thinking, the same diligence that characterized the efforts of previous Americans in situations of equal gravity.

It is quite possible that we could have survived as a nation, somehow or another, if some of the military problems of the past had not been solved. But I see no possibility that we can survive ultimately as a great world power if we don't solve our water shortage problem.

NAWAPA and other similar projects could well be a very important part of the total answer. At the very least, in order to meet our growing demand for water, we shall need a new and orderly program of moving water over great distances.

11 The Job Ahead

"Make no little plans; they have no magic to stir men's blood . . ."
—Charles Moore

America can solve its water crisis before it becomes a wide-spread, irreversible famine—if we act with bold imagination, determined resolution and a sufficient sense of urgency. It is not yet too late, but in a few years it *could be* too late if we merely talk and argue.

There is much to be done, and time is running out. In this concluding chapter, I shall try to outline those immediate steps by which we can move to meet the problem head on:

1. The very first requisite of an adequate national water policy will be a change in the public attitude. No longer is it good enough simply to know the *cost* of water-resource developments, unless we have a real appreciation for their *value.*

The old, cynical tongue-in-cheek attitude which looks upon water developments as so much boondoggling will have to go. It has long since outlived its time—if it ever had a time.

There are certain tired or unimaginative journalists in our country who never can refer to the Omnibus Rivers and Harbors development bills of Congress—or to the annual Public

Works appropriations—without trotting out again that weary, old, shopworn cliché, "pork barrel." The term is both inappropriate and misleading. The connotation it conjures of slimy manipulation and backstage connivery—or the impression that the water developments authorized in these measures are really somehow unneeded—simply do not square with the facts.

Water is life itself. It is the one thing we cannot do without. The time is rapidly coming in much of the United States when a community blessed with abundant, clean water will be better off by far than if it had oil or gold or uranium, or any other of the earth's resources, but lacked water. Insufficiency of available water reserves is the biggest single drawback to our economic and industrial advancement. Pure water, when and where you need it, is worth whatever it costs to get it there. Any soundly conceived program to foster this end is a very worthwhile investment for the United States or any of its governmental subdivisions.

Yet, to judge from the raised eyebrows with which various news periodicals sniff at the rivers and harbors program of the government, the uninformed reader would gain the wholly erroneous conclusion that the sole Congressional purpose for developing these latent and critically needed resources is merely to get certain members of Congress reelected. Such bills may or may not produce the latter result. Whether or not they do is wholly immaterial.

The point is that water developments pay for themselves many times over. The first $3.5 billion worth of Congressionally sanctioned flood-control works performed by the U.S. Army Corps of Engineers, already have saved calculable damages of more than $11 billion which would have occurred had they not been in place.

A new reservoir above Denver remained largely unfilled during two years of sparse rainfall. The critics hooted in glee. "Look what a waste the stupid government has committed with our tax dollars!" they scoffed. But *one rain* filled it up, bequeathing the city a store of water whose worth, at the going residential rates, comes to more than the cost of the dam. And from that one rain, the dam prevented measurable property damages far in excess of its cost.

On the navigable streams of the nation last year, more than three hundred new industries sprang up, adding greatly to the nation's employment potential and contributing to our rate of economic growth. Almost every water navigation project since the Republic's inception has generated a far greater stimulus to American commerce than had been anticipated by the careful and cautious criteria of the Army engineers at the time of the project's initiation.

An excellent illustration lies in the Gulf Intra-Coastal Waterway between New Orleans and Corpus Christi. When this development first was approved, the engineers officially anticipated an ultimate usage of some 7 million tons of commercial shipments annually. In 1964, less than one generation later, the annual traffic already had grown to an excess of 50 million tons.

The first prerequisite, then, is for the nation to rid itself of the albatross of negative thinking in the matter of water-resource developments.

2. We need a greater sense of *administrative* urgency than has heretofore characterized the slow, gradual development

of our rivers and streams. The U.S. Army Corps of Engineers has hardly a peer among the myriad agencies of our government in professional skill and expertise. But there are times when it really needs to get the lead out and move at a faster clip.

It takes entirely too long from the inception to the completion of a typical water development project of the Corps. The *average* time lapse between the passage of the survey resolution by Congress and the actual turning of the first spade of dirt, is an almost insufferable ten years and eight months.

After more than a decade of working with the competent and highly qualified representatives of this branch of the Army, my only real criticism is that they tend too often to *study* a problem to death. Surveys which—with just a little urgency—could be completed within one year ordinarily take three years to perform. The Corps likes to distribute its workload evenly by having a host of partially completed projects in the pipeline at all times. Distribution of the workload undoubtedly has some things to recommend it, but in my opinion it is carried to the extreme.

Certainly the long, laborious obstacle course of reviews and approvals by as many as eighteen different agencies of state and national government *after* the Corps has completed its final engineering report and *before* that report can be submitted to Congress for adoption is entirely too elaborate and cumbersome. This labyrinthine procedure has been known to consume as long as four years. A lot of this red tape should be cut.

The same criticism can be made with equal force to the Department of Commerce and to the Bureau of the Budget.

Just within the last few years, each of these agencies has arrogated to itself the unnecessary responsibility of second-guessing the Corps and duplicating many of the detailed studies which the Corps is much better equipped to perform —and in fact already has performed before the project even reached Commerce and the Budget Bureau. This is one main reason it takes so maddeningly long to get an Army Engineers' recommendation to the Congress where action can be taken.

In one recent instance, the Bureau of the Budget held and restudied for a full year and a half a project recommendation which already had been subjected to the careful scrutiny of eighteen different agencies and formally approved by each. At that, the Bureau only sent its comment to the Congress *after* the Congressional committee, despairing of ever receiving it otherwise, scheduled formal hearings on the engineering plan. And *then* the Bureau recommended "further study."

This is ridiculous! Like Kipling's "Old Men," we tend to

> Peck out and discuss and dissect and evert and extrude to
> our mind,
> The flaccid tissues of long dead issues offensive to God and
> mankind—
> (Precisely like vultures over an ox that the Army has left
> behind) . . .

We simply can no longer afford the luxury of delay.

3. Congressional procedures also need tightening. The long, exhaustive committee hearings which produce an omnibus bill, every three or four years, tend in the normal course of events to discourage the consideration of such compre-

hensive legislation on a more frequent schedule. Yet, tedious though these weeks of hearings admittedly are, the Congressional committees need to face up to the task of presenting water authorization packages on an *annual* basis, rather than triennially or quadrennially. Practically every other type of Congressional authorization is submitted annually nowadays. And few if any are more urgent than this.

The leisurely pace of the past is no longer responsive to the demands of the nation for development of our waters. Under the present practice, a project which finally works its snail-paced way through the administrative labyrinth and reaches Congress just a trifle too late for inclusion in an omnibus bill, is doomed to gather dust for three or four years until another omnibus measure is considered. In one case, a project involving flood-control benefits poked along and slept during a five-year period while the residents of the flood plain were driven from their homes on eleven separate occasions by the rising flood waters. Many of these people, unable to sell their otherwise attractive houses due to the continuing hazard, simply moved off and left them.

There ought also to be some device by which Congressional committees can approve smaller projects for actual construction without embodying them in the big, infrequent omnibus measures. Sensing the urgency of stepping up our pace, Congress in 1965 authorized a permissive plan in which Corps of Engineers projects whose total cost was below $10 million might be approved by resolution in the Public Works Committees of the House and Senate, and begun, without awaiting the slow arrival of an omnibus year.

President Johnson felt keenly that this constituted an infringement of executive power, since the President would have no veto authority over such individually sanctioned projects. He does have this authority, of course, over the big omnibus measures but does not possess the right of *item* veto. In other words, he must take the whole bill or reject it in its entirety.

Although such a procedure as outlined above has been legalized for a number of years with regard to federal buildings and upstream watershed projects of the Soil Conservation Service, regardless of their cost, there nevertheless should be some way to accommodate the President's understandable desire not to dissipate the executive power while still permitting more rapid action. Maybe we should devise a procedure for individual committee authorization followed by the right of executive review in each such case.

In any event, the Congress *can* speed up its own authorizing procedures. It should do so.

4. We need an extra head of steam behind the saline research and experimentation program, and behind our scientific inquiries into weather modification.

There is no question that the desalination program is worthy. Whether or not there really is anything to the business of artificially induced rainfall, it stands to reason that the sooner we find out, the better off we'll be. If it isn't a viable procedure in our present state of knowledge, then we can drop it or stick it away in mothballs. But let's at least put a little more emphasis upon the *inquiry*.

The alarming rate at which our underground water tables are declining clearly calls for a concerted effort, too long delayed, to find effective ways of recharging and replenishing the subterranean sands. Failure to develop such a program could end, ultimately, in the creation of an American Sahara.

If these things are worth doing, they are worth doing *now*. Delay at best will be costly. At worst, it could be fatal.

5. An enormously expanded pollution abatement effort on the national scale is long past due. We have the highly successful experience of the past decade upon which to build, and the public is ready for it.

As in many other pioneering pilot programs, we have gone slowly at first and gradually increased the tempo. The time is ripe for the antipollution fight to move into the main-event stage. The annual expenditure authorization of $150 million a year, as pointed out earlier, amounts to less than one dollar per citizen in annual taxes. The backlog of undeniable need and the continuing race against pollution warrant a much higher priority in our scheme of things.

The water-quality program could be doubled and tripled without afflicting serious financial burden upon any American taxpayer. With the health of the next generation and indeed our national future at stake, we will be derelict if we do not expand this program greatly.

In February, 1966, Senator Ed Muskie of Maine—on behalf of himself and seventeen other Senatorial co-sponsors—introduced a bill to launch a six-year crash program of $1 billion annually. Considering the estimate of $20 billion in expenditures needed to meet our clean-water needs by 1972, Muskie's asking is not one penny too much.

Inevitably, either the states or the federal government—

or both—will have to provide some system of *penalties* stringent enough to curtail willful pollution on the part of industries and others who could, but do not, clean up their wastes before dumping them into our streams. Perhaps, as a carrot to accompany the stick, the New York plan of an industrial tax write-off for money spent on waste treatment facilities deserves consideration.

Many industries have spent many millions in civic-spirited efforts to help. They merit our appreciation and should not be condemned in a blanket indictment of industry as such. There are some, however, that need to have the whistle blown on their callous disregard for society.

6. More emphasis should be placed upon the upstream program of land treatment and small detention dams in the tributaries. Already we have rapaciously exploited and rapidly exhausted some of our best farming lands. Next to water, the layer of topsoil which was our original legacy and national birthright is the most indispensable commodity in our natural inventory. As a people, we awakened late to the need for its conservation. All the more reason why, belatedly enlightened, we now should act with resolution to save what is left.

A very real food famine looms for much of the world. The time rapidly approaches when every single spoonful of topsoil that can be saved from erosion may quite literally be worth its weight in gold.

We already have stressed the way in which upstream land and water treatment conserves our investments in the big dams and waterways downstream. It is demonstrably a sound and needed program. In the language of the stock and bond market, it's a gilt-edged investment.

7. It is time to start planning in earnest on the best ways to facilitate long distance water transport. We have the clear water in cascading volumes going to waste. With just a little foresight we can be ready for the time when necessity will require us to move it to the areas where, within a few years, it will be desperately needed.

The NAWAPA plan merits sympathetic consideration. States and municipalities should get together within the various geographic zones of the country and assert what cooperation and statesmanship they can in planning for the maximum use of the untapped waters in their respective regions. State governments could well display some imaginative leadership in this field.

Inevitably, the federal government must come into the picture as a catalyst whenever local and regional planning hits a snag. A federal water transport authority may be the next step. Assistance, either in the form of matching grants or bond indemnification, will be required at some point in the relatively near future.

There is positively no limit to the heights which the national economy can reach if we attain a state in which the nation's water can be distributed to those areas where its lack has been a stranglehold upon the windpipe of investment and growth.

8. Coordinated planning must more and more replace the piecemeal approach which typified our early efforts. For too

long the nation in its attempts to develop our water resources was like the headless horseman. We rode off in all directions.

There still exists some jealousy among the Corps of Engineers, the Bureau of Reclamation and the Soil Conservation Service. Each considers its own program to be the best and most essential. *All* of them are necessary, and the time has come when they *must* abandon their suspicions and work together as members of the same team. Empire-building, so long a part of government and big business, must give way to the more important goal of getting the job done.

In addition to the three instrumentalities mentioned above, the Department of Health, Education, and Welfare has been active in the pollution field. Each has a role to play. None can do the job alone. All must develop smoother avenues for working together.

Similarly, states and cities need to abandon their hostility toward one another and their suspicion of the federal government. The job is so big that it will require the best that each has to offer.

Interstate compacts and regional planning commissions have blazed the trail for a coordinated assault upon the problem of water shortage. Multipurpose projects must increasingly replace the old haphazard crazy-quilt concept in which the waters of the land were developed in a disjointed and helter-skelter fashion.

In the Omnibus Rivers and Harbors Act of 1965, the very first provision of the law (Title I) sets up the machinery for a total concentration of efforts to produce an adequate and dependable supply of water for the northeastern United States. It is a model which well could be followed in the rest of the nation.

Under the primary direction of the Corps of Engineers, but with parallel responsibilities resting in each of the other agencies of federal, state and local authority, this program calls for the drafting of a master plan to see that everybody in the northeastern United States has access to an ample supply of pure water.

Components of the plan include: (1) a system of major reservoirs on all the river basins which drain into Lake Ontario, the St. Lawrence, the Atlantic Ocean or Chesepeake Bay; (2) major conveyance facilities for the *exchange* of water between these river basins wherever it is deemed to be in the national interest; and (3) major purification facilities to protect the quality of the water thus made available.

The comprehensive Trinity River development program authorized in the same law is a specific model of the coordinated solutions which can come about through such concerted planning. In this one package, the government has authorized a total development of a river basin for purposes of navigation, flood control, upstream soil conservation, recreation, water quality control and the preservation of fish and wildlife.

The Trinity program even includes an entirely new concept for recycling water by pipeline for more than a hundred miles from a huge reservoir in the middle of the basin back to the upper stretches where rainfall is less abundant, to assure continuous flow and quality protection. Thus the same water will be used over and over again. The drought-prone northwesterly stretches of the basin will benefit from the more plentiful rainfalls downstream, and the downstream inhabitants will never have to wonder if there is enough water on the plains to float their barges upstream.

This entire program will cost approximately $911 million, but it will serve more people than reside in any one of thirty-two states of the Union. State and local interests already have contributed $269 million of their own money to the river's development, and they have pledged an additional $256 million to match and supplement the federal share.

I believe a desirable degree of harmonious cooperation can be achieved without creating a new administrative super-structure, but if backbiting and interagency politics should threaten in the future to hamper the most expeditious and orderly development of our river basins, it may be that something like a water "czar" will have to be appointed to rap knuckles, knock heads together and cut through the jungle of red tape which too often has retarded the full development of the nation's pure-water potential.

We can whip the water crisis and forestall a water famine. But boldness must replace timidity. And we need to be getting on with the job.

The amount of water in the world is constant—unvarying and abundant. The total quantity has been precisely the same since the very beginning when, as the book of Genesis relates:

> ... God created the heaven and the earth.
> And the earth was without form and void;
> and darkness was upon the face of the deep.
> And the spirit of God moved upon the face
> of the waters.

An unending cosmic rotation steadily moves man's life-giving liquid by gravity through the gentle and incessant flow of streams to the great reservoirs of our oceans, draws it skyward by the sun's attraction to be purified anew, conveys it by cloud and wind, and returns it by rain to refresh the thirsty earth and renew man's lease on life . . . *ad infinitum.* It is an ever-recurring miracle, the most wondrous natural marvel of a wondrous universe.

Science can comprehend it, but never quite duplicate it. Man cannot change it. He can locally and temporarily befoul the process, and bring death. Or he can form a sort of divine partnership with nature, help it along—and preserve life. This is his choice.

We know that there is absolutely no such thing as *new* water; nor is there any conceivable limit to the number of times it can be used. Science tells us that the first glass of water you drank this morning contained some tiny molecules that fell in the flood of Noah, some that floated fishing craft in the Sea of Galilee 2,000 years ago, and some that washed blood from the beaches of Normandy on D-Day, 1945.

Science has given us knowledge. Where will we find understanding? And who will give us wisdom?

Twentieth-century America, like the prodigal son, has drawn heavily upon the bank account of its native endowment and squandered the substance in riotous misuse. More bountifully endowed than any nation in history, we've adopted the rather casual assumption that Providence protects America. We've extracted the riches of our natural legacy, exploited them to build a shining society, and wasted them in copious quantities.

Wasted! How this word runs like a refrain through the course of our national history—just a few seconds in the day of mankind, mere inches on the yardstick of Western civilization. In this brief span we've thrown away and destroyed more resources than most nations ever had. Most nations could live quite well on what we daily discard.

In the depth of New York City's water crisis in 1965, after four years of drought, it still could be reliably estimated that Gotham's eight million residents were *wasting*—through carelessness, leaking systems, and a legacy of irresponsible water management—almost as much of the vital fluid each day as London's seven million were *using*.

Our national past is a precious inheritance; our present, a glorious possession. Our future? Well, that depends upon us. If we are to have a long run future, we need to stop thinking of temporary food surpluses as a problem and look to the time, not distant, when our own burgeoning population will place great strain upon our ability to feed ourselves, let alone the famine-bent billions of a hungry world. And this means water.

If we are to stay apace in the growth of our national product and provide continuously in America the three million new jobs each year which our growing work-age population and automation's displacements demand, we need to look to our sources of energy to power the increasing requirements of industry. This, too, means water.

And if the new age of leisure which we're creating is to be a blessing rather than a bore, we must assiduously preserve what remains of our outdoor grandeur and the recreational magnificence of pure and unsullied waters.

In short, there is hardly any goal of our Great Society which can be achieved in the absence of a better stewardship for this, our most basic treasure.

We recall that other civilizations, also blessed with a spark of greatness, have strutted across the stage of world eminence only to fade and wane, their brief, bright promise unfulfilled. In the uncomprehending sand and heat of arid desert waste, their monuments lie buried.

Let no future archaeologist tell the story for us. We have the knowledge to tell it ourselves—if we have the wisdom. There is *enough* water to serve our needs for future time, if we learn to use and reuse it well. And there is *enough* time to do what we must. But there's not much of either to spare.

Index

249